Many thanks to the generous spo..........
who made this zine a reality:

Navabi plus size fashion retailer navabi.co.uk Smallsound/
bigsound effects pedal company smallsoundbigsound.com
Social Life social media agency @hellosociallife Studio Moross
design studio studiomoross.com and Margie McKinnon

Guided by the stories that you'll find here, we're proud to have chosen a
diverse set of charitable causes to be recipients of the funds raised from
sales of this zine. All profits are raised in aid of:

Mind provides advice and support to empower anyone experiencing a mental
health problem. Beat is the UK's eating disorder charity. Sisters Uncut stands
united with all women who live under the threat of domestic violence, and
those who experience violence in their daily lives. Centre for Mental Health
changes the lives of people with mental health problems by using research
to bring about better services and fairer policies. The English Collective of
Prostitutes is a self-help organisation of sex workers, campaigning for the
decriminalisation of prostitution, for sex workers' rights and safety, and for
resources to enable people to get out of prostitution if they want to. Sally
Burke's story is featured in The Cost of Care (pages 78-81). We will be
donating money directly to Sally and her mentally ill daughter Maisie for a
well-deserved holiday.

Art by **Petra Eriksson**

EDITORS' LETTER

I find it hard to get things done. It's not that I don't dream big – quite the opposite. I narrate cooking my dinner (practice for my TV show), I practise windmilling on my guitar (for my Glastonbury headlining slot), I mutter interviews with myself while I'm doing the hoovering (for Jonathan Ross). I think at some point, somewhere along the way, I stretched my ambitions so far out of reality almost as if to give myself an excuse not to try. Why bother, when all of my dreams are ridiculous! Why pick up my guitar, if I can't be Hendrix? Why make a pancake if I can't execute the perfect flip?

I had a dream I would write the perfect introduction to this zine. That I would do justice to all the stories within it. That it'd be so moving and eloquent and poetic that people would call in sick to work to stay home and read the entire thing, cover to cover. I thought that I'd talk about all the people I see in this zine – the ones who make music, or write about racial injustice, or look after and feed their friends, or design the pavements we walk on – and how they've suffered from mental health problems, and they've doubted themselves, but that I look at them and I'm awestruck and proud. I wanted to say that when I hear about their struggles with depression or anxiety or schizophrenia or bipolar disorder, and I see that they still talk to their friends, or crack a joke, or do their work, or even just get dressed or make a cup of tea – it often gives me the courage to give something a try. When they share their stories, even just to say "*I feel like I'm wasting my life*", I look at them and I see all the good. I see all the good and even in my darkest moment, I think: there must be good in me too.

Truthfully, I wanted to crawl under my desk to die when I opened up the blank Word document to start writing. I watched as my dream, like so many before it, whizzed out of my hands and deflated like a balloon that's been popped. Then I looked again at what this group of people had done. This group who are so often told – by themselves, by their mental illnesses, or by others – that they're not good enough. I looked at the pieces they'd written in the stolen moments when their self-doubt had quietened down for five or ten minutes, or an hour, or a day, and I remembered that sometimes, it only takes the tiniest spark of belief to move forward. We all need to try to remember how far those sparks can take us, and what they might mean to the people around us, who so often see all the good we can't.

Leah

"What's the point?"

I think this about a thousand times a day, but of course I have no answer. The point has a habit of slipping from my grasp just as I draw near to it. So when I ask myself, for the millionth time "What's the point?", what I am really doing is making a statement: I am lost. There is no goddamn point. It's a shrinking statement, and it makes my worries and interests and dreams smaller and smaller until I forget that they ever existed in the first place. Out of sight, out of mind.

It's especially difficult to find the elusive point of anything when the world is as it is. We live in a time when everything we felt sure of is crumbling, and the things we were certain would never, could never, happen again are rising from the earth like weeds. For people of colour, women, Muslims, trans people and all of the rest of us who don't fit neatly into this cisgender, straight, white world, things are tougher than ever. I have felt hopeless a lot in recent months, and the more that clammy chill of hopelessness has sunk in, the more virulently that unanswerable question "what is the point?" has sunk its roots into my mind. But with this zine, something began to change.

What started as a tiny fundraising pamphlet – just an article or two, a couple of recipes, some simple line drawings – has blossomed into a beautiful, affirming exploration of mental health today. I have read dozens of stories, some of which have held a mirror to my own experiences of mental illness, others of which have been compellingly strange and new. There are essays about feeling lost in the world, and comics about finding yourself. Each feature is as unique as the person who wrote it, but they all have one thing in common: they have given me a little bit of the answer to that question that's been spinning in my head. The point is survival, they say. The point is that mental illness doesn't need to be a death sentence. The point is the joy of a sizzling cheese toastie, or a hard fought-for recovery, or the love of a close friend. The point is the collage of a million tiny glimmering moments of happiness in our difficult lives. Don't let it out of your sight.

Ruby

This zine covers some difficult topics, from depression to alcoholism and self-harm. We think it's really important to cover these big issues thoughtfully and honestly. If you're worried about stumbling across an issue that's particularly upsetting to you, see page 166 for a full list of features and the topics they cover. You can also find a selection of helpful resources on pages 170-171 in case you're affected by any of the issues in this zine. Our amazing contributors are listed on pages 167-169.

ASK POLLY:
WHY SHOULD I GO TO THERAPY?

Heather Havrilesky writes the popular agony aunt column, Ask Polly, for New York Magazine. Each week, she cuts right to the heart of life's big questions, from "When will I feel worthy?" to matters of love, loss and death. Here, the queen of advice faces one of her biggest challenges: how can she help someone who doesn't want to be helped?

>>

No matter what question is put to Ask Polly's **Heather Havrilesky**, one of her go-to pieces of advice is "Get therapy." Whether someone has lost their job, is sinking into debt or has been deserted by their friends, there's always a value – Heather thinks – to looking inside yourself. When the world is crumbling around you, Heather wants you to sit in a small room, with a stranger, and talk. What gives? **Ruby Tandoh** and **Leah Pritchard** flung their most cynical questions her way. Could she convince them?

I have friends and family and a cat I talk to about my life. Why should open up to a total stranger?

When you talk to a friend or a member of your family, there's baggage there. You have preconceived notions about these friends and relatives – about their judgement, about their values. You have a history with them, you know how they operate, you know their blind spots. You also know exactly how much patience they have with any given topic. How do you tell your mother about the boyfriend you know she doesn't like as much as the last one, without getting preoccupied by how you should spin your story to make her like your boyfriend more than she does? The first and most immediate value of therapy is that it allows you to express your true emotions in a neutral, unconditionally supportive setting without kicking up any defence mechanisms, self-censoring, neurotic asides or worries about whether or not you'll be judged badly. The point of therapy, at least in part, is to explore your own feelings and deeply-held notions about the world in a context where that feels safe, where you don't feel remotely judged, and where the listener is trained in focusing, understanding, empathising and digging for the deeper roots of your feelings and your experience. Friends, family, and cats (EVEN CLAIRVOYANT WIZARD CATS) just can't serve in that role in the same way, and when you lean on them, you won't be nearly as free to discover who you really are, outside of your usual repeating messages to yourself about who you *should* be.

I got rid of all those 'shoulds' and dreams of being someone other than who I really am when I was in school.

New reigning notions of what you're doing wrong and what you should be doing instead come into circulation all the time, and unless you're very aware of your feelings and also aware of how those feelings are interpreted by your brain, you may be carrying around corrosive ideas about who you are and how you fail yourself every single day. As a citizen of a capitalist culture, particularly as a woman, a person of colour, or a member of any other demographic that isn't dominant, you're besieged by messages every day that tell you that the way you think, feel and function is somehow suboptimal if not pathological. Whether you're succeeding or failing, every dimension of your behaviour is scrutinised and second-guessed and pathologised to the point where you don't even need to hear new messages from our culture anymore – you reproduce all of that noise in your own brain. "You're too bossy," you tell yourself. "Remember how your dad and your ex both said so? You're too sensitive but you're also too hard on yourself. You're too aggressive but also too passive. You're settling again but you're also insatiable."

The messages you've metabolised contradict themselves to the point of being an incoherent chaotic mess of jabbering, but you still find yourself picking out whatever bits you can

You are meant to be in control at all times, these voices tell you, and yet when you do achieve control, that means you're not vulnerable enough

9

When people were direct and kind to me, I undervalued them because they looked me right in the eye and wanted to know things about me and it made me feel awkward

to keep defining yourself as inadequate and toxic. You can even do it with the clearly good things, like every talent you have and every pure, raw emotion you feel. You are meant to be in control at all times, these voices tell you, and yet when you do achieve control, that means you're not vulnerable enough, not feminine enough, and that you'll never find love as a result. Because our culture is very sick, we can't win no matter what we do. We're always getting it wrong.

Therapy isn't some nonstop symposium on the state of culture, mind you. But it is a pathway to your emotions and your deeply-felt experiences. By scraping away all of these messages and toxins and all of this negative self-talk, you can unearth your emotions and your instincts, and let them guide you toward what you truly want from your life.

But therapy is for really fucking sad people, though. I'm just normal-level sad. There's nothing interesting about me.

Never underestimate the many ramifications of being the boring kind of everyday depressed – or how interesting it can be to dig into the reasons for that depression! I was the boring kind of everyday depressed for years, and even though I had decent jobs and managed to make various relationships and friendships last, I was incredibly fearful, I wasn't ambitious at all, and I wasn't choosing friends and partners who were fully capable of showing up for me. Because I was ambivalent about myself and suspected that there was something deeply wrong with me, I brought that ambivalence into all of my relationships. I never asked for what I wanted because I assumed I didn't deserve it. When people were direct and kind to me, I undervalued them because they looked me right in the eye and wanted to know things about me and it made me feel awkward. It showed me how bad I was at really showing up for anyone else, and how bad I was at being truly seen and met by someone else.

When you're low-level depressed, in other words, your whole life is a patchwork of low-level depressed people. You consider these the most interesting people, but they've been selected primarily for their willingness to ignore you, to tolerate your flaws without really addressing them, or to reject and shame you over and over again in subtle ways that feel familiar because that's how your family operated, too. Meanwhile, that's also how you treat yourself. You're 'good' or 'bad' on any given day based on how much you achieve, how much people appreciate you, how good you look – all kinds of shallow, absurd criteria that have no moral weight beyond that which is imposed by your confused, needy head. You are ruled by circular thoughts and dreaded, half-felt emotions.

So many intelligent, highly sensitive people land there. And as they grow older, their emotions eventually start to eat them alive, and their mild depression turns into major depression and anxiety. Or they just stay low-level depressed but they never really get the careers or the lives they wanted, because all they ever had energy for was the minor drama of the week with this or that similarly unhealthy person. Blaming – storytelling about who's screwed everything up and prevented you from doing the things you 'should' be doing with your time – takes centre stage. The people you blame and have drama with are your scapegoats that keep you from looking closely at yourself and figuring out how to grow. Underneath your blame is a slow sinking feeling that everything you do is wrong.

But forget career and love goals. The most important thing about noticing and addressing your low-level depression is that you learn to feel your feelings – including your sadness, your fear, your joy, your longing. When you can feel your feelings, life goes from black and white to full colour. You aren't fully alive, in fact, until you've really learned how to

Happiness is all about figuring out how to savour the life you have right now – in all of its imperfect, unphotogenic glory

Digging into the past may feel bad at first... But over the long haul, what you're doing is relearning how to access both your sadness and your joy

let all of those emotions flow without constantly trying to control them or stop them. Happiness isn't about arriving at some 'best life' finishing line. Happiness is all about figuring out how to savour the life you have right now – in all of its imperfect, unphotogenic glory.

Ok, so maybe I'm sad enough for therapy. But won't everyone around me see it as some admission of guilt? They already think I'm a bit weird.

Allowing some room for other people to think you're deeply flawed and really weird is one of the most freeing and important things a flawed, weird person can do. Yeah, people don't like weird. That's because we live in a culture that's incredibly fearful – of anyone who doesn't have enough power or who could be seen as a so-called loser, of anyone who seems capable of disrupting the status quo. You don't have to say anything out loud or threaten anyone to scare them. You scare them just by being your true weird self. By owning your weirdness, you somehow make our sick culture less safe for fearful conformity.

So it's very important to know that this is the culture's problem, not yours. It's not up to you to explain your weirdness to everyone else. And in fact, the second you make peace with how weird and flawed you are, you will not only attract a whole swath of good people to your side, who want to know more about how you do what you do, but you will   make the world safer for the weird. This isn't something you inflict on the world. It's a light you bring into the world, by showing yourself the compassion that you deserve. When you are compassionate to yourself, you're naturally more compassionate to others. By forgiving yourself, you spread forgiveness and love.

What's the point of dredging up the past? I like living in the here and now. Just digging through all the shit of years gone by makes me so sad.

12

If your history makes you profoundly sad, that means you're carrying that sadness around with you all the time and probably wasting a lot of energy trying to keep that sadness inside. You're probably tired of trying to control it so it won't come pouring out all over the place. I used to be that way. Now I cry at everything and anything, and it's great. It's sometimes a little strange to be reading something in a café and have tears streaming down my face, but because I believe that our culture should include more open displays of emotion, I don't feel jittery about living that way and sometimes being seen as a freak for it. I know who I am and I like who I am and I also understand that I'm not about to change and become someone else through sheer force of will. This person isn't going away. I have to work with what she's bringing me. There's a lot of peace in accepting that.

Digging into the past may feel bad at first – and by at first I mean anywhere from a few months to years, honestly. But over the long haul, what you're doing is relearning how to access both your sadness and your joy. Because just as you've lost your connection to those really sad memories, you've also lost your connection to the happiness you felt in the past, too. And when you carry that weight around without acknowledging it, your ability to experience happiness and peace in the present is severely compromised.

People don't change anyway. And if people don't change anyway, what is the damn point of anything?

People's basic personality traits don't change all that much over the course of a lifetime. If you're a little oversensitive like I am, for example, you probably aren't going to wake up one day and feel impervious to what other people think of you. But that doesn't mean that I don't constantly recalibrate my behaviours and my strategies for dealing with the world and myself. Even though the basic outlines of my personality have remained the same since I was a kid, the way I use what I have has changed radically. When I was young, I used my

When I was young, I used my sensitivity to tell stories about what was wrong with other people... Now I try to use it to open my heart a little wider

Who are you, really, and what are your true gifts? What do you love? What makes you feel the most alive?

sensitivity to tell stories about what was wrong with other people, and I also used it to eat myself alive. Now I try to use it to open my heart a little wider. I use it in my writing and I use it to tune into what my kids are thinking and feeling. One benefit of clearing away cultural and deeply-felt, long-ago-ingested toxic messages about yourself is that you can see into your own heart for the first time, and you know what really matters to you (as opposed to all of the garbage you've carried around with you because you thought it would please someone else, but which really had nothing at all to do with your core values). If you feel lost and clueless, if you question the values and priorities of the people around you, if you feel a little frustrated or even disgusted with how you're living from day to day, those are good signs that you haven't done enough to explore what matters to you. Who are you, really, and what are your true gifts? What do you love? What makes you feel the most alive?

Oh god.

I get it. I used to be that way. But that's no way to live. And the benefits of facing those fears, and daring to dive into the emotional abyss can't be overstated. It will transform your whole life, and make things that you always thought were impossible feel possible for the first time. I know it sounds like I'm drinking and manufacturing and swimming through the Kool Aid at this point, but what can I say? Therapy is good for almost everyone.

So now you've convinced me I'm ready to sign up for therapy. Does that mean I'm going to turn into some simpering piece of sentimental lunchmeat with no edge whatsoever?

It will feel that way at first. But no one really loses their edge. It would be relaxing not to have that edge, but it never completely goes away. Chances are you'll flip flop back and forth between sentimental, weepy lunchmeat and your usual snippy, outspoken, caustic self, like I do. But honestly, who doesn't love a sharp-tongued freak with a soft, wilty little sap living deep inside of her? That's my favourite kind of person.

One of our culture's biggest flaws is that we're assumed to be one simple thing or another, instead of being the giant web of contradictions that every human quite naturally is. Our ideas about personality are now indistinguishable from our ideas about personal brands. If you're a serious writer, you should be very serious in everything you do. If you're a mother, you'd better act nurturing and kind to everyone. If you're a professional, you'd better not crack jokes or second guess yourself out loud. And if you're tough, you'd better never seem vulnerable.

But human beings are complicated. We contain multitudes. When you stand up for your right to embody the full range of emotions and thoughts and behaviours that make up the human experience, you're asserting the rights of all people to be who they are without apology. Being vulnerable, in our cruel world, will always come with an edge.

Therapy, ultimately, is about being given enough space by another human being that you eventually learn to take up space on your own. You learn to stand in the centre of the frame and say: I am just a human, flawed and complicated, but I am here, and I deserve to reach for a life that feels big and full and satisfying. I deserve to be seen and heard.

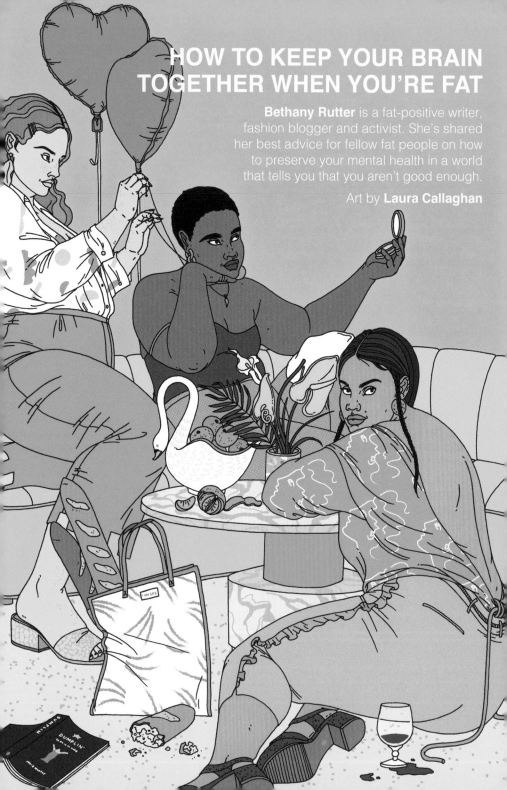

HOW TO KEEP YOUR BRAIN TOGETHER WHEN YOU'RE FAT

Bethany Rutter is a fat-positive writer, fashion blogger and activist. She's shared her best advice for fellow fat people on how to preserve your mental health in a world that tells you that you aren't good enough.

Art by **Laura Callaghan**

FIGURE OUT WHAT YOU WANT

When all around you are messages that certain things are not for you, it's hard to figure out how to live. A good place to start is to think about what you would want from life if you weren't constantly told that your experience is limited by your fat body. Who would you ask out on a date? How would you dress? Would you want to do a certain kind of exercise? Imagining these possibilities is the first step to building the confidence to live that life in practice.

DON'T PLAY THE GAME

Colleagues talking about their new juice cleanse? Sister telling you how many pounds she wants to lose before her wedding? Anti-fat talk is all around us, and it's rubbish. You are, however, well within your rights to say to someone: "I don't want to talk about this". It might feel confrontational to assert your boundaries in this way, but it's your prerogative. You don't have to play the weight-loss game just because it's being forced upon you.

(BUT IT'S OK IF YOU HAVE TO)

That said, standing up for yourself takes a lot of emotional energy. I always feel really depleted when I argue my case against someone else's fatphobia. It's truly OK if you don't want to keep fighting, and want to let the matter go. You're not letting the side down by not calling out every instance of fatphobia you encounter: it's the responsibility of fatphobic people to change their ways, and you don't have to make your life a constant education mission.

FEAST ON POSITIVE IMAGES

One of the very best things to do is to surround yourself with images of fat people living their lives. These depictions of full, happy fat lives don't have to be bare-all glamour and bikini shots. Simply following other fat people on social media can help, as can listening to podcasts like *Bad Fat Broads*, or reading those rare books that treat their fat characters with compassion and respect (I like Julie Murphy's *Dumplin'*). These connections will make your place in the world feel more stable, and less scary and alone. Plus, it's a great way to get to know people.

LEARN YOUR BODY

In lots of ways, becoming completely *au fait* with your body is the golden ticket to happiness. It's about getting to a point where nothing about your body can shock you. If the only images of your body that you ever let yourself see are carefully posed, lit and angled shots designed to minimise your size, then as soon as you're confronted with an image that contradicts that, you might have a crisis. Let yourself see your face and body from lots of angles. Look at yourself in mirrors a lot. Let other people take photos of you.

THE MONSTERS UNDER THE BED

Words by **Leah Pritchard**
Art by **Jasmine Parker**

It's in the very nature of a child to feel helpless or scared from time to time. In nearly every conceivable way, we rely on adults – most often our parents – for survival. We need to be given food, water, warmth, a place to rest. We need to be kept safe from harm. Someone needs to mop the sweat from our brow when we wake up from a nightmare, to pick up the broken glass from the kitchen floor, to tell the teacher we're being bullied. Children need to be protected, to be

reassured, and to be slowly taught how to do this for themselves. As they grow into their adult skin, the childish fears and helplessness naturally slip away.

It's embarrassing to admit that as an adult I feel as scared as ever.

My dad's foul temper manifested in a lot of creative ways. Remote controls that were low on battery got thrown at the wall. A dog that barked too loudly

It won't be surprising that my parents' marriage was tempestuous too. Me and my sister were rarely, if ever, shielded from their fights, which started before I was born and have never stopped (even after ten years of divorce). We were often neglected, sometimes actively targeted, by their sadness, their stress and their anger. We were terrified, and especially as children, had no power to make it better.

I was petrified when they fought. We would cower and cry in my sister's bedroom. We know that an animal under threat fights or takes flight, but with no means to fight and no exit, I was stuck with all of those feelings. What happened instead, when my body had to stay put, was that my brain made its own escape. I started to invent scary things. Visceral, blood-curdling horrors that were as far as possible from my own horrendous reality. It might sound counterintuitive, but for me, it was easier to face the man in the garden, the ghost in the mirror, or the bodies in the garage, than to try and contemplate as a child that the adults I looked up to, my examples of how to live in the world, were so often miserable, angry and cruel. It was easier to imagine a fictionally terrifying world – even one where I was being hunted or murdered – than to face the complex real-world horror of being neglected and let down. At least this was a role I knew exactly how to play.

near him in the park got a kick. A child who rushed into the same section of the revolving doors as him once got one too. If he'd taken a wrong turn in the car, we stayed deadly silent, because any reminder we were there was a prompt to him that we were to blame, and then there would be shouting and a hand raised. That was better, less mortifying, than when he would scream and shout at strangers who took slightly too long with a meter in a car park, or with bringing his bill in a cafe.

I became a really scared child. Too scared to sleep unless my head was underneath a thick duvet, even in the muggiest weather. Too scared to go to the bathroom alone at night, to pull back the curtains in my bedroom, to walk up the stairs unless my back was pressed to the wall, to ever be the person to turn out the light. I would lie in bed and pray, one by one, for each member of my family, including the names of every Filipino cousin I could remember (there are 50+), certain that if I missed one they would die. I would avoid the gaps between paving slabs, or make sure each foot stepped on the same number of bricks. I would imagine my parents and my sister being cut or stabbed, and I would desperately imagine patching their wounds. In those thoughts – those vivid, almost tangible imaginations – it was my responsibility to keep them alive.

The fear may be easy to understand, but it was no less excruciating for it. It also seemed to reflect on me in ways that only added to the pain. When I imagined someone crawling out from under my bed and cutting me open, I knew that I was (and always had been) an inadequate wimp. When I daydreamed about my family being dismembered or shot, I knew I must be broken somehow, destined to be an abuser or a murderer.

I recently started therapy. I told my therapist about when my fears had started. Under her instruction, I closed my eyes and tried to remember being six years old, terrified, hiding under the covers. She asked what it looked like. I replied that I was staring at the bed, watching the tiny me cower. She explained that by imagining myself watching from a distance, rather than putting myself into the shoes of that scared six-year-old, I was creating a distance between myself and the overwhelming power of the fear I had felt. On some level, it was too frightening to me to even relive it from the safety of the therapist's office. She told me to imagine entering the room as me now, as a brave adult, and to comfort the child. I felt tears welling up but I tried my best to hold them in. I put myself in the room and knelt by the bed. I kissed that child's forehead. I checked the cupboard for her, and under the bed, and out the window. I told her she could keep the covers over her head if it felt best that way.

I'd always known it, somewhere deep down, but now I could see clearly what I had desperately needed back then. I gave her understanding and reassurance. She fell asleep and I carried her warm, sleepy body to my car. I took her to safety.

It's been a difficult journey to this realisation, but I now believe it wholeheartedly: my brain has always had instincts to keep me safe. When it was too frightening and too sad to think about my parents not loving me enough or, eventually, about my dad leaving, I channelled the fear and sadness that pooled in my body elsewhere. When I was scared, unable to run or fight, I froze – I sunk into my imagination, making up fears

The most important thing to me now is that I no longer see these fears as something that's broken in me.

or catastrophising, or I turned off completely. Sometimes my eyes glaze over and my brain turns off, even now, even if it's something as simple as being a bit anxious or bored at a supermarket checkout. I got so used to dissociating as a child – that is to say separating mind and body – that I still do it all the time, at 26.

I want to interrupt this two-decade trend. I don't want to fear the dark. The most important thing to me now is that I no longer see these fears as something that's broken in me. I'm proud that the small child with so much to be scared of was able to turn that into something she could understand. She kept herself safe by switching herself off, by looking away, by thinking up the ways she would fight for her family. Those coping strategies are the ones I still rely on, even now.

Maybe this is just the way I'm wired. It's the way my brain helped me to survive, in the best way it knew how. In time I'm sure I'll be able to unpick this strange little circuit, at least a bit, by facing the real-life anxieties I had then and the ones I have now. I'll learn to deal with them face on. I've started to do that already. But even if I never fully rid myself of these thoughts of abduction and violence and torture and death, I won't let myself be ashamed in their wake. It was OK to be scared when I was small, and it's OK to be scared now. There is so much to be scared of.

"PRICELESS"

BY JAMES CHAPMAN
FROM ANONYMOUS. WWW.SOUNDIMALS.COM

I got my first job after dropping out of university.

Being able to look financially stable made me feel strong.

THESE ARE ON ME!

I'd buy drinks for people

but I was struggling.

I sold my things to raise some cash.

Yet soon enough I'd find a way to spend it.

It was a mental struggle. I couldn't tell anyone.

[DENIED]

So after rejections from credit cards...

I got a short term loan

at the time it felt like pure magic.

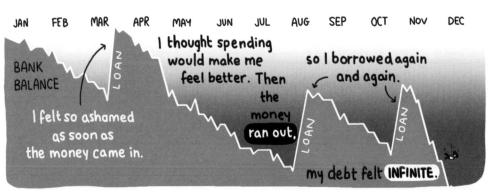

PUSHING THE BINARY

Non-binary people are neither male nor female: they may be both, exist somewhere in-between, or fit neither category. Non-binary poet and perfomance artist **Travis Alabanza** talks about how they have found it difficult to access judgement-free mental healthcare. Art by **Rudy Loewe**.

"Are you a boy or a girl?"
"Are you a boy or a girl?"
"Are you a boy or a girl?"

I am asked this for the eighth time today. I wonder if the question hurts more each time I hear it, or if it is the exhaustion of the day that causes the final question to induce tears.

People ask me about my mental health a lot. More specifically, they tell me how I can get better. They give me advice on yoga classes, healthy eating and getting out of bed before 10am. They tell me to keep in contact with at least three people a day. They give me lectures about how if the sun is out it will make me feel well. Sometimes they send me pills – supplements and herbal remedies – in an attempt to chemically coerce a smile.

I even go to the doctors, and they prescribe me medication. I pretend to use it for a while. Then I actually use it for a while. I stop taking it for a while. I repeat the process. The doctor refers me for therapy

sessions. The therapist talks to me about coping mechanisms, how to relax, and alternative ways to recover from trauma. They tell me to breathe deeply.

Through all of this, I am asked, assumed, probed, told, forced to act in a gender that has already been decided for me. I am reduced to boy parts and man feelings: big lumps and bulges, gulps past the Adam's apple. The doctor's office doesn't have a box to tick for my identity, and the therapist called me a "brave young 'man'" after I explained to them a part of my childhood. Already, despite 50 minutes being left on the clock, I knew the session had ended.

We can't talk about mental health until we sit with the pressure and pain that a gender binary creates for transgender individuals everyday. How do I tell a doctor that the reason I am upset is that the world has forced me to become something that I never asked for? How can I explain that I am trying to recover from past traumas, but I am being

retraumatised every day? The weight of gender is all-encompassing.

When a chicken burger is thrown at me at in broad daylight, when I'm called a 'tranny', when I'm being tripped up on the tube or called a "freak in a dress", my cisgender (i.e. not transgender) male doctor cannot comprehend it. There is no self-care technique for someone whose very existence is anathema to the society they live in. I cannot be healed while mental illness and gender non-conformity are seen as pathologies. The world bolsters my mental illness when it questions, denies and negates my gender.

A doctor asked me what was wrong.
I said, "I can't go to a doctor because I do not trust you."
He said, "Why?"
I said, "Because from the moment I was born, you told my mother a lie that has created pain for me ever since. How can I trust the people who condemned me to a life of manhood?"
He said, "We are following orders, systems, structures."
I said, "And isn't that the problem with care?"

We were both told to breathe deeply.

BAD BOSSES

Being your own boss isn't always as dreamy as it sounds. Music journalist **Laura Snapes** shares her top tips for staying on top of your mental health when you're self-employed.

Art by **John Allison**

I've had some bad bosses. The cinema manager who made me watch *The Simpsons Movie* eight times in a day. The hapless smoothie bar owner who asked me for a loan so that we could pay for that day's fruit. The misogynist bully. The one who made me work at a soup-smeared desk from 6am to midnight without brushing my teeth or changing out of my pyjamas.

(That last one was me.)

Being your own boss is sold as the ultimate professional goal: the chance to dictate your workload, control your schedule, and answer to no-one. It can be glorious. I write this from under a blanket, while listening to ABBA's back catalogue in consecutive order. But what nobody tells you is that you could easily become a crueller boss to yourself than anyone else could ever be – something it took me over a year to learn.

You might blow off engagements with friends to get more done, and feel bitter when they're all hanging out without you. You ignore the looming suspicion that the whole point of work, once you've paid rent, is to earn you the capacity to have a life. Perhaps you ditch physical activity too, and feel the low groan of your thigh muscles wasting away as you mash out more work.

Working like this is the opposite of clarity. It's more like mania. I eventually reached a point where I'd overworked myself so badly that the whole concept of work stopped making sense. I knew I had to try and build in safeguards to stop it ever happening again. I wish I could say I became a model boss overnight. In truth, it took me months.

I share my tips proudly, but you should follow them with trepidity: other people's guides on how to live a fulfilled life can be as detrimental as they are well-intentioned – the struggle to match their level of organisation and happiness is its own form of pressure. But I hope that you can tailor these ideas to your own life, rather than looking at them as a rigid instruction manual.

RECOGNISE WHEN YOU'RE LAPSING INTO UNHEALTHY HABITS

Write a list of the things that you do when you're letting work overtake you. For me, it's things like not showering, forgetting to clean my teeth until way after lunch, obsessively picking non-existent blackheads on my arms, getting in a social media spiral, eating lunch at my desk, binge-eating, scouring the cupboards for snacks even when I know there aren't any, not reading, not exercising, not making plans, and scheduling more work on top of the work I already have. I use pitching as a form of procrastination, which is self-defeating idiocy of the highest order. Whatever your patterns are, recognising them is a good way to start breaking them.

MANAGE YOUR SOCIAL MEDIA USE

Social media may not be an issue for you. I have an addictive personality, so services that constantly update are catnip to me, and I have to restrict my use of them. There's a free app called SelfControl that allows you to restrict access to any websites you like for a set period of time, which you can't break even if you restart your computer.

CREATE ROUTINE

Artists like Nick Cave famously keep 'banker's hours', treating creativity as a routine rather than sitting and awaiting the muses. If you can stick to set hours, do it! But the unpredictability of self-employed life means sometimes that's not possible. In its stead, establish other unbreakable routines, based around the times of day you work best. I know that if I don't exercise first thing, I won't do it at all. My friend Charlotte goes for a walk around the block first thing every day. I eat the same thing for breakfast each day, and lunch, because I flail in the face of too much choice. If it helps you, set times for meals and hot drinks breaks.

STAY ON TOP OF YOUR BUSINESS

Do your accounts once a week so you don't have to figure out how you were going to justify that KitKat Chunky three months after you ate it – and read up on everything you can expense as a self-employed person in your particular field. Keep a spreadsheet of your assignments, income, invoicing and outgoings so that you know what you're doing (are you doing too much?), how much money you're going to earn, and when to chase people who haven't paid up (I find Google Docs helpful for this, so I can access it if I'm away from home).

RECOGNISE WHEN WORK JUST ISN'T COMING

Sometimes, for all your best intentions, work just doesn't happen. That can be horrifying in the face of strict deadlines, but if you have a little time, get away from your project for a bit, and have a routine of things you do at times like these. I might read a chapter of a book, go to the supermarket, or sort out some other chores, because I live in a really boring place where fun isn't immediately available. If you live somewhere more bustling, you might go to a free exhibition or for walk in a park.

MOVE YOUR BODY...

If you're physically able, moving around, whether outside or to YouTube yoga, makes your brain feel good. Scientists talk about endorphins flooding your body after a good workout. For me, the pleasure is about doing something so strenuous or repetitive that I can't think properly: swimming dissolves my brain; my poor co-ordination means that any classes require total concentration otherwise I'll fall on my face; and when I run, I listen to my favourite podcasts. Moving your body doesn't have to be about changing it, though as a writer – a job without fixed progress or easy rewards – feeling my muscles change and my capacity increase is a linear pleasure that I don't get from work.

A couple of years ago, I interviewed Kathleen Hanna (of the band Bikini Kill) about how she makes music while living with chronic illness. I asked her what advice she'd give to anyone whose health condition keeps them indoors, and she had a lovely answer: "Think of something that you can do, as opposed to all the things you can't do – and do that. It's just like gardening: what can grow in this soil? There's some soil you can grow roses in and some soil you can only grow cactuses in, so if you can only grow cactuses, become the best cactus grower in the whole world. Taking care of yourself is the most important thing. Find something that makes you happy, like looking at beautiful pictures, or, if you're able, listening to beautiful music, or sitting by the window and looking outside – small things like that can be absolutely huge. Don't get down on yourself that you can't run a 5K or dance all night long at a fun club. Give yourself a break."

...AND IF YOU CAN'T

Awareness of mental health issues in the workplace is terrible here in the UK, and the thought of telling someone that you can't do the work by the time they want it is scary. You may well have to deal with totally unreasonable people who don't understand what you're going through, which sucks. In my experience as a freelancer and former full-time editor – and this is of course totally anecdotal, not a rule – people would rather know in advance that you're going to miss a deadline than chase you after it's gone. When I've had to ask an editor for more time, they've always understood and been accommodating.

ASK FOR THE TIME YOU NEED

MAKE SURE YOUR WORK ENVIRONMENT IS AS YOU LIKE IT

Even self-styled slobs become clean freaks when it comes to working from home. How could I possibly even start to think before I launder all my clothes, change the sheets, and deep-clean the bathroom? On a Sunday night (or at some quiet juncture before you start a new series of tasks) make sure your zone is spruced. Doing it regularly means you'll stop making yourself the star of a DIY episode of *How Clean Is Your House?* Also, if you have enough space, try not to work in the same place as you sleep.

There are all sorts of studies about how the harsh blue light that your computer and phone screen emit messes with your melatonin levels, which you need to sleep. Try to turn them off and do something else for half an hour before you go to bed. And if you can, avoid sleeping with your phone in your room.

TAKE A BREAK FROM THE SCREEN BEFORE BED

FOOD FOR THOUGHT
PART ONE

Recipes for life from **Diana Henry**, **Izy Hossack** and **Yossy Arefi**. Art by **Anna Valdez**.

MUMBAI TOASTIE
DIANA HENRY

Toast is often the thing we turn to for comfort, but a diet of it – which one can depend on when low – isn't such a great idea. Not only does it get a bit sad, but making an effort to do something more interesting means you are taking better care of yourself and have the pleasure of noticing the smell and flavour of other ingredients. Chopping coriander and squeezing lemons will make you feel better before you've even tasted this sandwich. This recipe comes from my good friend, Roopa Gulati, and I'm addicted to it. It's Mumbai street food.

FOR THE FRESH CHUTNEY
½ green chilli, deseeded and chopped
Handful of coriander leaves
Leaves from 8 sprigs of mint, torn
1 garlic clove, crushed
Sea salt flakes
½ tsp caster sugar
Juice of ½ lemon

FOR THE SANDWICH
2 slices of white bread
50g cheddar, or similar cheese, grated or very finely sliced
1 tomato, sliced
¼ small red onion, very finely sliced
Pinch each of ground cumin, coriander, ginger and cinnamon
Butter
¼ tbsp oil, to fry (if you don't have a toasted sandwich maker)

Put everything for the chutney, except the lemon juice, in a mortar and pound it with the pestle. You can just chop everything together instead, but the chutney is better if it has had a good pounding. Add the lemon juice.

Spread the chutney over both slices of bread. Lay the cheese, tomato and onion on one of them and sprinkle with the spices. Top with the other piece of bread.

If you have a toasted sandwich maker, use it, buttering the outside of the sandwich as usual, or melt a knob of butter and the oil in a frying pan and cook it over a medium heat for about three minutes on each side, weighing it down (I use a flat saucepan lid with a heavy can on top). Be careful not to burn the sandwich, and adjust the heat accordingly. The cheese should melt. Serve immediately.

CINNAMON ROLL PULL-APART LOAF
IZY HOSSACK *(TOP WITH CINNAMON)*

For a while in my teenage years I had a troubled relationship with food, assigning different foods moral values according to the 'health' level they had. It wasn't until one summer, when I spent a few weeks shadowing a food stylist, that I escaped the grip of that mindset and I fell back in love with food – the beauty of it in both creation and eating, and the value that each and every ingredient holds in a recipe. I was surrounded by the joy of food and I let it engulf me fully. On the last day of working with the stylist's team I brought them this loaf of coiled, pillowy bliss and we shared it, tearing the layers apart with sticky fingers.

1 tsp fast-action dried yeast
60ml lukewarm water
80ml milk, any kind
50g unsalted butter
2 eggs
180g plain white flour, plus
more for kneading
180g wholemeal bread flour
¾ tsp salt
50g granulated sugar

FOR THE FILLING
150g dark brown sugar
2 tbsp ground cinnamon
1 tsp cornflour
55g butter, melted

FOR THE GLAZE
85g icing sugar
Milk
½ tsp vanilla extract

Dissolve the yeast in the water in a large bowl and set aside for 5 minutes. Meanwhile, gently heat the milk and butter together in a small saucepan, just until the butter has melted. Remove from the heat and let this cool slightly.

Pour the lukewarm milk mixture into the bowl with the yeast mixture and stir together. Mix in the eggs until smooth. Add the flours, salt and sugar and stir to get a shaggy dough. Tip out onto a work surface dusted with flour and knead it, dusting with flour to prevent sticking, until smooth and slightly tacky – about 10 minutes.

Place the dough in a greased mixing bowl, cover, and leave in a warm place until doubled in size – about 2 hours. While the dough rises, make the filling by combining the dark brown sugar, cinnamon and cornflour in a small bowl.

Once the dough has risen, roll it out on a lightly floured work surface to a 40x40cm square, then brush most of the butter over the entire surface of the dough, reserving a little to grease a 1lb loaf tin. Sprinkle the filling mixture evenly on top, then roll it up tightly into a log. Cut the log into 20 pieces, each around 2cm thick.

One by one, lay each piece of dough cut side down on a floured surface, dust with more flour then roll into a 9cm circle. Stack the circles, then lay this column sideways in the greased loaf tin. Cover with oiled cling film and leave in a warm place to rise for 30 minutes. Preheat the oven to 180°C/fan 160°C/gas mark 4.

Once the dough is ready, remove the cling film and bake the loaf for 35-45 minutes until dark golden on top. Leave to cool for a few minutes before running a knife around the edge of the tin to loosen the loaf, then tipping it out onto a cooling rack.

Make the glaze by stirring the milk a little at a time into the icing sugar in a small bowl until you get a thick icing. Mix in the vanilla extract then spoon the glaze over the warm loaf. Serve warm or leave to cool completely. Eat it by tearing the layers apart with your hands!

ANY FRUIT GALETTE
YOSSY AREFI (APT. 2B BAKING CO.)

The kitchen has always been a centre of calm and peace for me – a place that makes sense, even when the rest of my life feels totally chaotic. It is a place where I can focus intensely while also being totally creative and free, a true rarity. Time spent slicing, kneading, and stirring can quiet my mind when the rest of the world is not, and in these anxious times, the comfort of the kitchen is more important than ever.

A recipe I know I can always turn to is the humble fruit galette – a casual, open-faced pie sort of thing made from buttery crust and any seasonal fruit that's around. I can make a galette just about anywhere without any special equipment. I've even been known to sneak away while on a group vacation to take a moment to breathe, and make a galette or 5…

You can make a galette with just about any seasonal fruit – try berries or sliced stone fruit in the spring and summer, and in the cooler months try sliced apples or pears, cranberries or even concord grapes. Taste the fruit and use just enough sugar to highlight its natural flavour, and make sure to bake it until the crust is deep golden brown and the fruit juices are bubbling.

1 disc rye crust, recipe follows
775g seasonal fruit
75-100g sugar
Seeds of one vanilla bean
1 tbsp flour
Pinch salt
Squeeze of lemon juice
1 egg, for egg wash
Crunchy sugar

Preheat oven to 220°C/fan 200°C/gas mark 7. Line a baking sheet with parchment paper.

Roll the dough out on a lightly floured surface to a 30cm round just under 5mm thick.

Add the sugar and vanilla bean seeds to a large bowl and use your fingertips to evenly work the seeds into the sugar. Stir in the flour and salt, then add the fruit and lemon juice and toss gently to combine.

Move the dough to the prepared baking sheet. Pile all of the fruit in the center of the dough, leaving a 5cm border around the edges. Fold the edges of the dough up and over the fruit and press gently to seal the folds.

Chill the galette until the dough is very firm, about 15 minutes. Then brush the dough with a beaten egg and sprinkle with sugar. Bake until it's a deep golden brown and the fruit juices are bubbling. Cool slightly before serving.

All pie crust is made from the same basic ingredients: flour, fat, water, and salt. I am partial to an all-butter crust because I think it tastes the best. The key to flaky pie crust is to keep the ingredients nice and cold – especially the butter and water – and to work quickly and intentionally. The small amount of apple cider vinegar in this recipe helps tenderise the dough by preventing the gluten in the flour from forming long strands, making the dough tough. I like to mix pie crust with my hands rather than a food processor or pastry blender because I can control the exact size and shape of the butter pieces for the flakiest results.

170g plain flour
170g rye flour
1 tsp salt
255g very cold unsalted butter
1 tbsp apple cider vinegar
8-10 tbsp ice water

Makes enough for one double crust pie or two galettes.

Whisk the flours and salt together in a large bowl, cut the butter into 1.5cm cubes, and add the apple cider vinegar to the ice water.

Working quickly, add the butter to the flour and toss to coat. Then use your fingers or the palms of your hands to press each cube of butter into a flat sheet. Keep tossing the butter in the flour as you go to ensure that each butter piece is coated with flour. The idea is to create flat, thin shards of butter that range from about the size of a 5p piece to about the size of a 10p piece. If at any time the butter seems warm or soft, briefly refrigerate the bowl.

Sprinkle about 6 tablespoons of the icy cold vinegar–water mixture over the flour mixture. Use a gentle hand or wooden spoon to stir the water into the flour until just combined. If the dough seems dry, add more cold water a couple of teaspoons at a time. You have added enough water when you can pick up a handful of the dough and easily squeeze it together without it falling apart.

Press the dough together, then split it in half. Form each half into a disc, and wrap each disc in plastic wrap. Chill the dough for at least 2 hours before using, but preferably overnight. It keeps for up to 3 months in the freezer wrapped in a double layer of plastic wrap and a layer of foil. Thaw in the fridge before using.

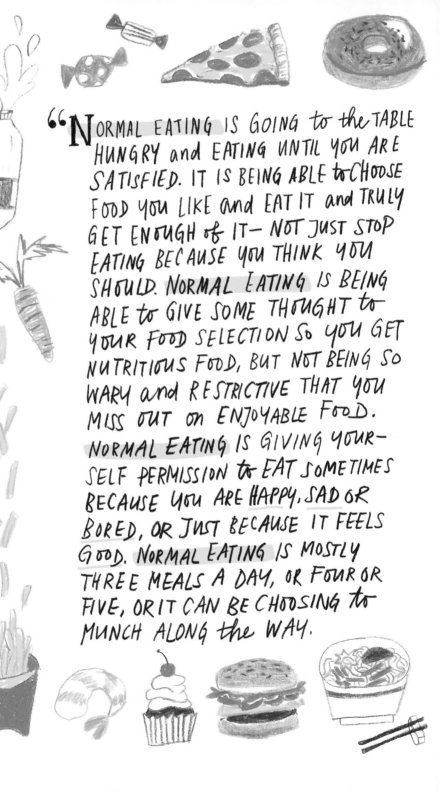

"Normal eating is going to the table hungry and eating until you are satisfied. It is being able to choose food you like and eat it and truly get enough of it— not just stop eating because you think you should. Normal eating is being able to give some thought to your food selection so you get nutritious food, but not being so wary and restrictive that you miss out on enjoyable food. Normal eating is giving yourself permission to eat sometimes because you are happy, sad or bored, or just because it feels good. Normal eating is mostly three meals a day, or four or five, or it can be choosing to munch along the way.

IT IS LEAVING SOME COOKIES ON the PLATE BECAUSE you KNOW you CAN HAVE SOME AGAIN TOMORROW, OR IT IS EATING MORE NOW BECAUSE THEY TASTE SO WONDERFUL. NORMAL EATING IS OVEREATING AT TIMES, FEELING STUFFED and UNCOMFORTABLE. And IT CAN BE UNDEREATING at TIMES and WISHING you HAD MORE. NORMAL EATING IS TRUSTING YOUR BODY to MAKE UP FOR YOUR MISTAKES IN EATING. NORMAL EATING TAKES UP SOME of YOUR TIME and ATTENTION, BUT KEEPS ITS PLACE AS ONLY ONE IMPORTANT AREA of YOUR LIFE. IN SHORT, NORMAL EATING IS FLEXIBLE. IT VARIES IN RESPONSE to YOUR HUNGER, YOUR SCHEDULE, YOUR PROXIMITY to FOOD and YOUR FEELINGS. 99 — Ellyn Satter Institute

PEARL LAW

MOVING ON

Crystal is a Canadian girl who found acceptance in the roller derby community – one of the few sports where she is allowed to participate completely, and with full support, as a transgender girl. Her story was told in acclaimed 2014 documentary film *In The Turn*. Crystal's mother Karen explained what roller derby means for her daughter's mental health: "Crystal still really struggles because you really can't undo the damage of being excluded, but roller derby has introduced her to a community of people who have her back, people she can still write to and talk to and who encourage her, some of whom were once where she is now. Community like that is so important when dealing with the struggles she has."

In the documentary, we see the lives of other LGBTQ roller derby players unfolding alongside Crystal's journey. The film's director, Erica Tremblay, is a roller derby player herself, and found that the sport's ethos of acceptance and zero tolerance of bigotry afforded her a safe space to explore the potential and the power of her body. "Having control over your own body is a powerful thing. Roller derby was such an incredible healing tool for me. I am a survivor of sexual assault and roller derby gave a safe space to work through my relationship with my body. As I skated and improved I felt like I was taking true ownership of my physicality. It was a safe space for me to be. I think that is why a lot of people are attracted to roller derby. You are able to work through things with the support of other people who want you to succeed, both on the track and in your life."

UP

Exercise can be a powerful tool in maintaining and improving our mental health. Here, **Ruby Tandoh** shares her own story and talks to three other people who have first-hand experience of how moving your body can work wonders for your mind. Art by **Molly Brooks.**

I lived for several years with eating disorders before slowly – with the help of my friends and partner – finding my way towards recovery. I eventually reached a healthy relationship with food, but making peace with exercise still scared me: how was I supposed to reconfigure this thing, which for so long was a tool for me to control my weight, and make it a positive, nurturing act? Exercise had been a negation for me – it was measured in calories burnt, weight shed, time spent away from the temptations of the kitchen cupboard. I wanted to change that.

I was lucky enough, during my time at university, to share a flat that was just five minutes away from North London's biggest climbing wall. On an uncharacteristically courageous whim one weekday evening, I signed up for a taster session, and exercise became a colourful, joyful thing. It was tough climbing those walls, but I fell in love with it. I loved the boyishness that I could channel in my loose jeans and t-shirt, hanging precariously from the walls by my fingertips. I loved how strong I felt, and the way that my body, for the first time, began to feel fully mine. I felt powerful. I had no idea how many packets of Quavers added up to an hour on that climbing wall, and I didn't care.

"Roller derby has introduced Crystal to a community of people who have her back, people she can still write to and talk to and who encourage her, some of whom were once where she is now."

Jessamyn Stanley is a yoga instructor working in Durham, North Carolina. As a fat black woman, she defies many of the stereotypes of what it is to be fit. She presents to us a different vision of health: one that's a far cry from the largely white, slim and blonde fitness gurus of Instagram. She has been outspoken in encouraging other fat women to embrace their fatness, to be unapologetic and to exercise (or not) whenever, however they wish. In a world where fat women are encouraged, or even forced, to lose weight in order to gain acceptance or to be allowed access to even the most basic healthcare, this is a radical act.

Yoga has had a huge impact on Jessamyn's confidence, allowing her to divorce exercise from the idea of weight loss, and she proudly advocates the same for others. On her website, Jessamyn describes how her "mental clarity" and overall emotional stability have benefitted since she started practising yoga. For Jessamyn, the question when it comes to exercise should be "How do I feel?" – not "How do I look?".

Emma Yates is an instructor who works with elderly people to help improve their physical fitness. She has found that the social element of the sessions she runs is just as important (or even more so) than the physical workout. "For one lady, the session is her only weekly activity. Coming has helped her get to know people, and discover more about the area."

These kinds of exercise groups are particularly effective when it comes to the problem of falling. "What can happen when people fall is that the fear of another fall leads them to restrict their activity levels, leading to increased social isolation. Their muscle strength reduces and increases their risk of falling – a vicious cycle." This makes it crucial that elderly people are given support to maintain mobility. One programme to help prevent falls among elderly people resulted in increased confidence, reduced anxiety and fear, and a return to playing with grandchildren. In short, an overall improvement in mental wellbeing.

PATIENCE
by **Alanna McArdle**

No one could believe
what kind of run what
kind of
collapse
was to occur

In one of many waiting rooms
a half-drawn sketch

How could any patient here
be proud enough to
show the broken strokes
like it was a finished
piece?

And to be honest
I don't know why
we even bothered taking
turns
to count the benefits of pain

mild
moderate
severe

they said it
would allow you sleep and rest

to breathe remembrance of
a bodily entirety

relief

       to mobilise your grief

positive thinking

       repositioning.

NO CRAIC

The idea of the tortured artist is a persistent one. But what happens when depression doesn't hand you your masterpiece after all? **Ellis Jones** of Trust Fund writes about how mental illness stole his craic, and his music.

Art by **Chloe Emiabata**

When I was 23 I decided that I could no longer take antidepressants because they were stopping me from writing songs. Rather, they were stopping me from writing good songs – songs that connected with real life, and reflected that experience in a way that was artistic and meaningful. I had been taking citalopram for a couple of years, and although the antidepressant had taken the edge off my depression, it made me feel like I was stuck in neutral.

I hated the way that this, as I saw it, repressed my creativity. By reducing the amount of instability in my life, citalopram had taken away what I felt to be a vital tool for my songwriting. I needed instability to write songs, I thought. It's a common belief, and I fell into it wholeheartedly. I didn't come off my medication slowly, as I perhaps should have done. I just stopped, cold turkey, and settled down ready to write a banger. It turned out that creativity wasn't as simple as that, though. I spent the next year self-harming, drinking excessively and being a dick to my friends. I didn't write a single song.

The belief that depression fuels creativity is common in discussions of art and music. But for every wistful paean to Kurt Cobain or Elliott Smith, there are also people writing thoughtfully against this kind of naive romanticism. I count my experience as evidence to support this argument: clearly depression and creativity aren't linked in a linear way. But at the same time, the fact that the two things feel so linked maybe suggests that there is something there worth exploring, a complex and nuanced result of creativity and depression both relating to ideas of self-worth, identity, and communication.

For me, depression is often about a failure of communication. When I am depressed, I feel as though I have no 'craic'. I think about this word 'craic' a lot. My friends say it – a less divisive alternative to 'banter'. It's perhaps easier to define it in the negative: we talk about people who are nice but boring as having 'no craic'. Depression, for me, is having no craic. It is a time when the good and funny thoughts just aren't coming – my brain has stopped making them, or has stopped sending them to me. I am in a different gear to the people around me, and I feel guilty for them having to talk to me, and for them having to engage with someone who is giving nothing back.

Music is a language that is broader and more universal than speech. It can say things that are not possible to say with words. It can be both more abstract and more literal than language. So songs would seem to offer a very good outlet for 'talking' about failure of communication – a way to communicate when the other ways are blocked. They offer an alternative for when speaking to people doesn't feel possible or useful. But for me, the depression blocks this outlet just as thoroughly as it blocks the others. When I feel like I need to write songs the most, that's exactly the time when I know for sure that I can't and won't.

The problem is that songs are obviously still a form of communication, and as such they come from a place of being ready to engage with the world. Even when they are angry, despairing, or envious, they are grounded in that need to connect with others. In order to write songs, I need to be able to imagine myself wanting to talk to somebody, or to listen. Everyone's experience of mental illness is unique, but for me it is really important to understand that there are times when I won't be able to make music, however hard I try.

Not being able to do something you love is frustrating. I feel that frustration keenly when I'm depressed. It often leads me to be less open to other people's music, and critical of the music 'scene' in general. It makes me bitter and selfish. Over time – I have been writing songs for maybe fifteen years – I have, hopefully, got a little bit better at dealing with this. Realising that this lonely, depressed, pessimistic place isn't where I'll make my best music has helped me to weather the storm. I can sit back; I can take the time to heal.

Another way that I have learned to deal with these spells of depression, and their impact on my creativity, is by reconfiguring the type of authorship I see myself having over my songs. When I am feeling bad, it helps to remove myself and my identity from the songwriting process as much as I can, even though the end result is, to some extent, always about the self. I try not to think about my agency.

It helps me to think about the ways in which authorship is linked to larger structural and economic changes. The idea of art as the unique output of a creative genius is an over-simplification, to say the least. The invention of the printing press in the 15th century led to copyright laws that placed a greater importance on the artist; Romantic ethics positioned the artist as an outsider critic of mass-culture; the development of recorded sound allowed the global proliferation of music as an exchangeable commodity; rock music moved institutional criticism to inside a commodity-based mass culture; mass communication created a global popular music. Each of these developments shaped the philosophy and culture of the time, and the creative outputs of the people who lived and worked within that time. We can't escape our circumstance.

In this way, I like to think about writing songs as determined almost entirely by factors beyond my control, so the songs do not represent my special thoughts and feelings, but only my location in time and place. They – and I – are a product of this society. The songs become less about my ability to communicate and less about personal social relations. They are still my songs, but they have their roots in something much bigger than me. It's not always possible to do this. But at the best times, when I have somehow removed the element of personal self-expression, songs feel like a puzzle that I have set myself. It becomes about me trying to work towards a solution. I present it to myself, and I feel proud.

KISSING DOORKNOBS WITH MARA WILSON

Mara Wilson is a writer and performer whose memoir *Where Am I Now?* tackles child stardom, mental health and the tricky business of love. **Ruby Tandoh** talked to her about how she came to open up about her anxiety and OCD, and why representation matters for people with mental health problems.

Art by **Ana Galvañ**

I'm in Los Angeles. I was getting really bad seasonal affective disorder in New York and somebody pointed that out to me, like, "Have you noticed that you're always depressed?" And I was like, oh yeah, maybe that has to do with the weather! [Laughs] So now I'm here for the winter I guess. I never thought I would come back.

I read your book, Where Am I Now?, *and I loved it, and what really struck me was this knack that you have for storytelling. Do you think these things are bound up together – your acting and your writing? It seems to me like they're both a way of telling a story.*

I think that storytelling is just the way that I think, and process things. There is something human about putting a narrative to everything – I think that's something that a lot of us do anyway. One thing that I noticed when I was young was the way my inner monologue changed when I was reading, then acting, and then when I was writing. Like when I was young, I started reading books, just non-stop, and I would be writing stories in my head. And then later on I noticed that I started having little dialogues with myself back and forth in my head. I think that was because I was reading so many scripts and I was doing so many interviews. I think that I'm lucky that any way I can tell a story, I'm happy. The performing was only one part of it, but that was the part that I sort of went with for a while. Later on I realised that wasn't going to really be enough for me.

By your own account, though, sometimes these stories become scary. You lose control of this narrative you started, and the story you've written pulls you along in a direction maybe you hadn't planned.

That's a really great observation. I think that definitely was a problem. It's always been said that humans are pattern-seeking creatures and I've even heard that people who tend to think, you know, conspiratorially, it's almost as if their brains are working a little too well? They're overworking, they're finding patterns where there are none. I mean people have done that about my life too. People say, "Why did you quit acting? Was it because you were too ugly to work in Hollywood anymore? Did nobody want to work with you? Did you have something traumatic? Were you pregnant?". I think people invent stories when they don't understand what is going on. They want to fill in the gaps. But I think that with a mind affected by obsessive compulsive disorder (OCD), like mine, that's a dangerous thing, because you get fixated on it. It becomes compulsive. I was born with these tendencies, I was born with this anxiety. I was always a nervous kid.

My girlfriend, Leah, is really similar. When I was reading in your book those passages about how scared and anxious you were as a kid, I just kept thinking at every sentence: "Oh my god, that's Leah". You must have had loads of people come forward saying that your experience resonated with them.

That has been people's favourite chapter, I would say. I've got the most response from it. People will tell me, very specifically, "This encouraged me to get help." When I was writing that essay I kept stopping in the middle of it to break down and cry because I think, for the first time, I saw myself from the outside. I saw this eight year old child who was suffering and who needed help and couldn't get it right away. There were people around who were trying to help, but they didn't understand. It was sad for me, it was painful for me. When I sent it to friends and family members, they had similar reactions. It was very intense for them.

I actually remember when I was first diagnosed with OCD. I was still kind of in the public eye, I was still doing movies. I promised myself that when I was an adult I would go out there and I would talk about my OCD, because I was desperately looking for other people out there who had it. I was looking for celebrities who had it. I was trying to read up on it as much as I could. There wasn't as much out there as there is today. I said, I'm definitely going to do this when I get older, because I want to help people. That was always a goal of mine. And I'm glad that I finally got the chance to do it.

There's an amazing circularity there, because you describe how it was reading a book, *Kissing Doorknobs*, by Terry Spencer Hesser, about a girl coming to terms with her OCD, which gave you confidence that you weren't alone in your experience of mental illness. And now you've done the same for other people.

I've had people say, "Your book is to me what Kissing Doorknobs is to you". And that's an incredible feeling.

That book helped me so much. I really wanted to step forward in a way and be able to do that too. I've had people say, "Your book is to me what *Kissing Doorknobs* is to you". And that's an incredible feeling.

48

I think that a lot of times the media sensationalises it. There's even a movie out right now about Disassociative Identity Disorder [*Split*, directed by M. Night Shyamalan] and that's not how it works, you know. It's gutting to think that this is something that we're still misconstruing. I think there's been a lot of talk about anxiety but I think there are conditions – things like bipolar disorder and schizophrenia and even personality disorders – people don't quite understand, people are still a bit afraid of. We need to see more depictions of it, and we need honest accounts of what it's like to deal with these things.

But I think we also need to normalise it, in a way. We need to show that, you know, you can be a person living with a disorder and it's not that much different than having diabetes. You treat it. That's still something that is very important. I've always wanted to write a character where it's like – oh yeah actually I have schizophrenia but I take my meds and I'm fine. Not – oh no this person has schizophrenia they must be either somebody who you feel sorry for, or a monster! Which is the way that they're often portrayed, which is horrible and not true. It's completely inaccurate.

What ways would you suggest for people who want to open up about their mental health to their parents or friends? Because you talk in *Where Am I Now?* about using *Kissing Doorknobs* as a translator or an intermediary – you show it to your friends, your school psychologist, your dad, and that acts as a talker in a sense.

I think that was how I did it, I used the book as a translator. I would say: "I have the same thing that this character has in this book." I would tell my friends to read it and they would. I do think that's why representation matters, why you need it in books and TV, why that can definitely help people. A lot of times friends or partners don't really want to believe it. That is a big issue. They don't really want to believe that you could be going through such pain.

I think the way to frame it is: "I want to get help." If you are able to, say that: "I want to get help." That definitely is a way. This is something to tell your friends about, and if they are truly your friends, they know *you* and they already know these things about you. They're going to love you and care for you no matter what. Putting a name on it doesn't change anything, really. It doesn't change who you are.

I think we are getting better about it. We are realising that something like one in four people deal with some kind of mental illness. It's something that's a lot more common. And even people who don't suffer from mental illness, they are going to deal with things themselves sometimes. Most people will encounter these things in their lives.

That's absolutely something we wanted to stress in this zine – that mental illness can affect anyone. It's something that you can have, and you can work on, and you can live your life around it, you know?

I think that we don't want to think about the hard times. I definitely have that issue myself. I remember, especially when I was younger, if somebody saw me when I was having a bad day, when I was having my panic attacks and I was crying, and then they would say something like, "Oh hey Mara, I saw you were upset the other day", I would give them the cold shoulder, like I don't want to talk about that. There's that.

I think that it's really how you look at it. I use a mood tracking app and it definitely confirms my suspicions that I have seasonal affective disorder because I looked back at January and February of two subsequent years and it was just all, on a scale of 1-10, threes. Before, I had started feeling really upset when I had to track that I was having a bad day because I felt like that ruined things, you know, like that ruins my week. I noticed that I was still stuck in this pattern of thinking that having a bad day ruins everything. Or having a bad day is a bad thing. It felt much more freeing when I looked at that app and I said to myself, no, you're allowed to have bad days. You are allowed to feel crap. It's going to happen, it's going to wax and wane like that. Even if you aren't dealing with serious mental illness.

It's also something very much in American culture where we are told that we need to strive for happiness all the time. But I don't think that's a very good goal. Happiness is an extreme. I think that we should strive for contentment because happiness is like if you eat candy all the time. Then it doesn't matter as much anymore. But if you strive for contentment, that's really sort of the best thing to do. That's definitely what I'm trying to do. Allow yourself to feel bad sometimes, I think acceptance is really key here. "OK, I'm feeling this way, and I'm now going to go on with my day despite it."

That's good advice!

You have to take it one day at a time. You know, it's funny. I look back on my life and I think of some happy memories I have, and I realise that they were times that I was going through something really difficult – but there was sort of a break in the difficulties and the pain – and I was able to have a good time despite it. Those memories I really treasure, because they stand so starkly in contrast to how I was feeling. That's something that I've been thinking about a lot lately.

This interview has been edited and abridged for clarity.

Mara has worked with Project UROK on resources for people suffering from mental illness. Project UROK was founded in 2014 by writer and comedian Jenny Jaffe, and hosts videos on topics as diverse as Asperger's, depression and domestic abuse. It's a resource for teenagers and young people of all ethnicities, faiths and sexual orientations. You can find their videos or donate to the project at projecturok.org.

Mara's memoir *Where Am I Now?: True Stories of Girlhood and Accidental Fame* is available in all good bookshops.

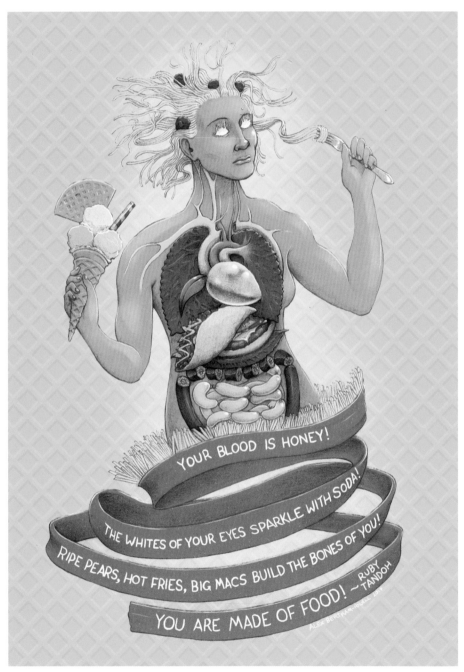

Art by **Alex Bertram-Powell**

PROS & CONS

BY SAMMY BORRAS

I ALWAYS LAND ON MY FACE.

I FELL OFF MY BIKE A COUPLE OF YEARS AGO.

I FRACTURED MY JAW,

BROKE SOME TEETH,

AND RIPPED OPEN MY BOTTOM LIP AND CHIN.

THE WEEK BEFORE I FELT VERY FREE.

I'D BEEN SELLING COMICS AT THOUGHT BUBBLE IN LEEDS,

AND THEN WENT STRAIGHT TO LONDON TO SEE THE PIXIES WITH SOME FRIENDS.

WOOo!

WHEN I WAS OFF WORK AND ON A LIQUID DIET I HAD TOO MUCH FREE TIME ALL OF A SUDDEN.

I KEPT THINKING ABOUT MY MORTALITY, AND HOW FRAGILE MY BODY IS.

BUT BRAINS ARE WEIRD – ODDLY THE INCIDENT DIDN'T MAKE ME ANXIOUS ABOUT CYCLING AT ALL.

I WAS BACK ON MY BIKE AS SOON AS I COULD AFTER MY FACE HAD HEALED.

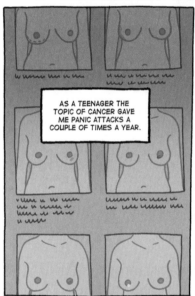

AS A TEENAGER THE TOPIC OF CANCER GAVE ME PANIC ATTACKS A COUPLE OF TIMES A YEAR.

AFTER THE ACCIDENT THIS STARTED TO BECOME DAILY PROBLEM.

UH! JUST CONCENTRATE!

5, 6
9, 7
8, 4

MY HEALTH ANXIETY GOT OUT OF HAND, AND THE ONLY THING I COULD DO TO TAKE MY MIND OFF THE SUBJECT WAS MATHS PUZZLES.

EVENTUALLY I WAS REFERRED TO COGNITIVE BEHAVIOURAL THERAPY (CBT), WHICH WORKED WELL FOR ME.

WHEN I WAS UTTERLY CONVINCED MY LIFE WAS ABOUT TO END I STARTED LIVING MORE IN THE MOMENT - WHICH HAS ITS PROS & CONS.

I FOUND IT VERY DIFFICULT TO PLAN COMICS AND CONVENTIONS.

I WONDER IF SARAH CAN SELL MY COMICS IF I DIE BEFORE AUTUMN CONVENTION SEASON?

BUT WHY WOULD ANYONE BUY THE FIRST ISSUE OF A COMIC IF I'M DEAD AND THE STORY WILL NEVER BE COMPLETED?

BUT I STARTED SKATEBOARDING - SOMETHING I NEVER HAD THE GUTS TO DO AS A TEENAGE GIRL.

I STILL DON'T KNOW HOW TO DO ANY TRICKS, BUT I REALLY LOVE CRUISING AROUND IN THE SUMMER.

SONIC THE COMIC (THE BAND)

DO WHAT YOU WANT

Words by **Sadhbh O'Sullivan**
Art by **Ruby Taylor**

Near Liverpool Street station in London, there's a series of winding alleys, harking back to years ago when the City was jumbled and built on top of itself. In the mornings, on my way to work, streams of people hot-foot it to their office chairs, huddled over their Pret A Manger filter coffees. But at the end of the day – no matter what day – my walk home stutters as I try to find a way through the crowds of people. From the moment the clock hits 6pm, people clutching pints spill out of the doors of the area's dense cluster of pubs, restaurants and bars. The narrow streets fill with loud, tipsy bodies.

Drinking is an easy coping mechanism to fall into. Why wouldn't you want a way to disconnect and unwind? Or crave something to loosen the knots that tighten in your brain over a working day? We are all so tired, and drinking feels good. Great, even. It makes things seem simpler. Laughs flow faster. Silence feel not awkward, but comfortable.

Because drinking is so easy, it is everywhere. To even hint at a less palatable truth about alcohol is to bring something recreational face to face with something ugly and messy: addiction. Because of this, and because of how ingrained drinking is in British society, it's intimidating to even admit you're attempting some kind of sobriety. As the 'other' in this situation, it can feel like you're a fun sponge. Wanting to slow down, or even stop, is tough.

Maybe your hangovers have gone from a reminder of a fun night to a piercing migraine. Maybe you started drinking alone and don't know how to stop. Maybe you just don't enjoy it like you used to, but you don't know how to be with people without it. Whatever your reasoning is, it's legitimate, and it's ok. So how do you get out of the habit?

1 BE HONEST WITH YOURSELF

Acknowledge how much you drink, when and where. Not the amount you tell your GP, or your parents, or your partner, but the actual amount. This can be a terrifying bit of mental maths, but once you have it in front of you, making the change becomes about the practical ways you can bring that number down instead of the monolithic idea of "drink less".

If possible, it's also important to be honest about why you're buying those canned G&Ts on the way home. Was it boredom? Fear of feeling alone? Fear of being with people? Is it tied into your mental health? Drinking to excess is often symptomatic of a bigger issue. Cutting back or stopping may help you to focus on the problem at hand.

2 BE HONEST WITH OTHERS

This one can be the hardest. The moment you talk about not doing something that's seen as 'normal', it calls into relief how others do this 'normal' thing. It can feel like an attack on other people's drinking decisions. It isn't. It's for and about you, and the people who are important to you should be able to understand that. Once it has been established among the people that matter to you, it gets easier to turn drinks down.

3 BEING BORING ISN'T BORING

The idea that it's boring to leave early and go to bed is a lie we started telling ourselves when our parents let us stay up one New Year's Eve to see the fireworks. Nothing fun happens in the last hour of the party, anyway. What's more, it's wonderful to be wanted at the end of a night instead of endured.

4 PRACTISE BEING SOBER WITH OTHERS

Re-acclimatising to enjoying yourself sober, the way we did when we were kids, is surprisingly hard. Any anxiety you might have about a situation has no chance of being dulled by two pints in ten minutes anymore. It can be like re-learning to have friends. Start during the day, when it's more normal to not be drinking, and do small, sober things with friends. Plan an afternoon where all you do is drink coffee and talk about your favourite series. Go to the cinema. Just sit in the same room and read. Try to find ways to get comfortable with people sober, before moving into the more dangerous night-time socialising.

5 CREATE ALTERNATIVES

Herbal tea is a really good option for weeknights. Make sure that non-alcoholic drinks are available at the place you're going. If they're not, try for a different venue. Work out your go-to sober pub drink (lime and soda is a common choice for a reason: it's both tasty and really cheap). The more often you choose non-alcoholic drinks, the more normal it will feel, until a glass of red wine on a Sunday night feels heady instead of the obvious choice.

6 CUTTING DOWN ISN'T CUTTING OUT

It's not an either/or situation: you don't have to see this as the be-all and end-all if you don't want to. Let yourself make mistakes. If you decide not to drink one night and then do, don't beat yourself up. You're not weak. This is just part of how we learn to be kind to ourselves and prioritise our wellbeing. Embrace periods of sobriety, enjoy drinking when you want to and always, always listen to yourself. As the nurse at my doctor's surgery once told me, "You are worth taking care of."

When talking about my mental health I often feel like I'm running in circles around the things I want to say. There is nothing that can describe what it feels like to wake up crying. Not wake up *then* cry, but to have been crying in your sleep then wake up, face and pillow wet. To have a hurt so deep and so sore that you can't tell where it ends or where it began. So you might understand why I use placeholders.

The benefits office told me I've been reported for suspected fraud texted to a friend while hyperventilating, duvet over my head, jaw clenching so hard my teeth are squeaking, is a placeholder. It's not just being reported by some petty-minded busybody who thinks that claiming £70 odd a week is a game to me and that under my bed I have a pot of gold that I dip into when needed. The sentence is the start of an essay my soul wants to write, that talks about what it's like to be a grown woman with no savings, a lot of debt, a degree that has no career prospects, no partner, and a body incapable of staying stable long enough to hold down a desk job.

The words I want to find live behind that sentence. They scream about what it means to know that the benefits office don't need to have any proof to support their accusation, that they can just call me a liar and stop my payments. I would have to steal food to supplement what the food bank gives me. I'd have to give up therapy appointments, because I can't afford the £15 a week. Unable to afford the bus fare, I'd have to stop picking up my medicine. It would mean giving away my dog, losing my flat, moving into a hostel. I try not to imagine beyond there.

I'm sad and I'm alone and I don't know what to do anymore written in a notebook while sat on a hot marble bench in the park is a placeholder. If I could draw, the page would just be a gaping dark void, a hole with no ending, where good things and good people fall and never hit the bottom. It would be wet tears on a birthday card. A car ride back from a gig where I played music and smiled at beautiful people the whole way through, then cried until my taxi driver asked if I wanted him to pull over. Instead of my chubby thighs leaving sweaty imprints on the bench there would be a groove where the heaviness of my feeling weighed me down.

I miss you whispered at the end of a Skype call is a placeholder. The words bigger than *miss you* are too silly. They won't come from my Dick Van Dyke-sounding voice. These words won't tell you how it feels not to have you at the end of my arm, or in the next room. They can't tell you what it means to worry that this is the last time we will see each other: this pixelated voice stuttering over a bad connection might become my last memory of you. I know there'll come a time when I miss you all the time and I'll miss not just the presence of you, but the everything about you. And worse than that, that one day I won't miss you at all.

Sometimes, however, I find the words. I manage to string them together and somehow, out of this hell that I'm in, someone else hears me. They hear me not just in the blurted-out words, but beyond that, to the place where there is nothing, just my pain and I. They offer me a hand and I reach upwards, even if I can't quite grasp it yet.

SISTERS UNCUT

Domestic violence and poor mental health are often linked: domestic abuse can contribute to mental health problems, while those suffering with mental health issues are often vulnerable to domestic abuse. 64% of survivors of domestic and sexual violence suffer from PTSD. Ignoring these issues can be deadly.

Sisters Uncut is dedicated to ensuring the government does not fail women when they are at their most vulnerable. We believe it is essential to women's safety that refuges are trained and able to deal with the mental health issues that survivors often suffer from.

Art by **Eve Archer**

THE PRICE WE PAY

Poverty, insecurity and social isolation can create and exacerbate mental health problems. **Rosamund Pearce** sets out the costs of living with mental illness – perhaps being unable to work, forced to perform your disability in order to receive benefit payments, and being left unsupported in times of mental ill health – in a society that prioritises productivity over people.

1,109,309

Number of three-day emergency food packages distributed by Trussell Trust food banks in 2015-2016.

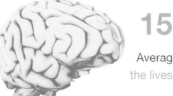

7,000,000

Estimate of the number of people in the UK using high cost credit, such as a payday loan.

1 in 4

Number of adults that experience at least one diagnosable mental health problem in any given year.

Three quarters of these receive no support at all.

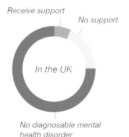

Receive support

No support

In the UK

No diagnosable mental health disorder

15-20 years

Average number of years cut off the lives of those with severe and prolonged mental illness.

INTO THE DEPTHS

Autistic people suffer suicidal thoughts at greater rates than the general population, and yet are pressured to maintain a facade of 'normality' by hiding their autistic behaviours and personality traits. **Martha Rose Saunders** looks at how the pressure to 'pass' as non-autistic impacts her mental health, and how she finds peace in the depths of the ocean.

Art by **Robin Bray**

I've had the same recurring nightmare since I was very young. In it, I am falling through the ocean into the depths, where giant squid hang, suspended like pale, repulsive angels, and a thousand strange and shapeless things move unseen in the darkness. It is the dream I dread the most.

This nightmare has often confused the people close to me. The ocean has been one of my lifelong special interests: as a child I pored over marine biology encyclopedias, obsessively memorising names and collecting facts. I loved the Pacific red

octopus with its three hearts and constantly shifting, kaleidoscopic skin; humpback whales with their haunting songs which never repeat; the ancient Greenland sharks that drift for as many as 400 years below the creaking Arctic ice with glowing parasites instead of eyes.

It doesn't make sense to others that the ocean, which brings me such pure, enthralling pleasure, could also be my greatest subconscious fear. But it makes sense to me. This all-consuming fascination, known as a 'special interest', is one of the most well-known traits of autism, and anything that reminds me that I am autistic, or may convey it to others, is tainted with shame.

High-functioning autistic people are often able to navigate the world in ways that other autistic people perhaps cannot, blending in socially and living and working independently. The ability to 'pass' as non-autistic is often considered a benefit or privilege. In reality, this endless performance of normality is exhausting and degrading.

What's more, autistic girls like me exist in a particularly strange and dangerous contradiction. Women are taught their primary value is in their desirability; autistic people are publicly desexualised, infantilised, and stripped of dignity. This juxtaposition leaves autistic women in a constant state of desperate self-construction, obsessively chasing an elusive ideal that can only be obtained by attempting to completely erase any trace of our disability. John Berger once wrote "the surveyor of woman in herself is male"; the surveyor of me inside myself is also neurotypical, the traces of my neuroatypical autism erased. Even when completely alone I am always monitoring myself, a warm, sickening rush of self-disgust and humiliation washing over me when I do something visibly 'autistic' like stimming. Stimming is short

for self-stimulatory behaviours such as rocking, fidgeting, or feeling certain textures; it's a soothing method autistic people use to manage feeling overloaded or anxious. Like many high-functioning autistic people, I have avoided the stigma attached to

these behaviours by adapting my stims to appear as subtle as possible, replacing flapping my hands or rocking with picking and peeling back the skin on my cuticles until they bleed. Self-mutilation is preferable to the shame I associate with more stereotypical stimming.

Such aggressive self-policing is actively encouraged even by supposed autism advocates. The majority of parenting advice prioritises hiding an autistic child's symptoms over accepting them, and autism specialists have suggested that high-functioning autistic women should not seek diagnosis or support if they can 'pass' as non-autistic. These comments are made despite research showing that two thirds of adults on the autistic spectrum have suicidal thoughts, and 35 percent have either planned or attempted suicide. Given our deeply ingrained sense of shame and the constant pressure to perform and conceal, these figures are unsurprising. To say that we are vulnerable to mental illness is almost too passive: poor mental health and rock-bottom self esteem are practically built into our brains, a logical consequence of growing up knowing that your very essence is shameful and must be hidden.

The cost of living your life as a constant performance of togetherness is that it becomes fatally dangerous to fall apart. I am terrified of speaking to mental health professionals, as I have grown up associating the inability to repress my inner self completely with failure. I often feel as though if I start to cry I will never be able to stop, and that the careful chrysalis I have spent my life building around myself will shatter, leaving exposed something I am not quite ready to confront yet. For autistic women, admitting that we need help doesn't just require self-acceptance, but a deeply painful and introspective deconstruction which goes against everything we've learned to do to survive.

Imagining a future without this debilitating shame often feels impossible when right now I'm even embarrassed to be alone with myself. But I'm learning, slowly. I recently went on a date to the aquarium, somewhere I would previously only ever visit alone. It's a strange place to feel at your most vulnerable, but in the soft blue glow of the shark tanks I felt more naked than I ever have in my life. Just a year ago it would have been inconceivable to me that I would share such an intimate part of myself with anyone, let alone a man whom I wanted to fall in love with me. I don't know if I'll ever be able to feel completely comfortable with myself, but I've stopped having nightmares about the ocean. Baby steps.

LAUGHING ABOUT PNEUMONIA

How can we tell the ones we love the most that we're suffering? **Esmé Weijun Wang** has a habit of laughing at all the wrong moments. She takes a look at the ways in which we use humour to diffuse the feelings that hurt us. Art by **Danielle Chuatico**.

I was diagnosed with pneumonia while on a family trip last week to New Orleans. We'd had one lunch at Commander's Palace, me in my best pink beaded dress, feeling somewhat swoony, but able to hold things together enough to tuck into some shrimp and grits and two sips of a gin martini. Things went awry from there. What I'd thought was a cold, or bad flu, progressed. I began to wheeze and to feel a rattling in my chest. Soon, I was having a hard time breathing at all.

The last time I sought urgent medical care in New Orleans was in 2012, when I was shipped to a most unpleasant psychiatric hospital for ten days, so I was comparatively pleased to be listened to, assessed, and then told that I had pneumonia.

The boyishly handsome doctor said "[he'd] like to prescribe, in addition to antibiotics, a steroidal…". But I'd tuned out after the word "steroidal."

"Oh, I can't take anything steroidal," I said. "I have schizoaffective disorder, bipolar type. So steroids are something I avoid."

"Ah," he said, seeming mildly baffled at the disclosure. "Yes. They can induce mania, in some cases. Well, there's something else I could put you on instead, but this one does run the risk of hypervigilance as a side effect..."

"NO." I perhaps said this more loudly than I needed to. "I really don't need any more hypervigilance than I already have. I also have PTSD."

At this point, I was beginning to feel more like a good ol'-fashioned Mental Patient with Too Many Diagnoses, and not so much like a Pneumonia Patient, who, as far as I know, do not carry significant cultural baggage.

"What from?" he asked, by which he meant, From what did you acquire post-traumatic stress disorder.

I might have paused here for a number of reasons. My PTSD seems to have originated from a number of sources, and I didn't feel like going into them with this man at the urgent care clinic. I also wondered why he felt this to be an appropriate question. Who cares why I have PTSD? Knowing that was not going to improve either his care of my pneumonia or my back-in-California psychiatric treatment. So even though I could have told him that it was none of his business, I just said, "Rape."

And then... I burst into giggles.

**

The significant traumas in my life have passed, and yet my physiological and psychological responses to them have only begun to truly interfere with my life this year. I'm used to becoming isolated by my mental health, and by people's reactions to it: the depression and psychosis that I live with carry a great deal of stigma. But when it comes to trauma, and discussing the symptoms and triggers of my post-traumatic responses, the isolation is unlike any I've ever felt. And that's without even going into the details of the actual traumatic events that scarred me, which even the saintliest soul likely finds hard to stomach. Trauma, and in particular sexual trauma, has profoundly isolating effects in Western culture.

We find it difficult to talk about trauma. It is difficult to be a human and to learn about the brutality that other humans are forced to endure.

In spite of, or maybe because of, my personal understanding of trauma, what that means and how it feels, I struggle to hear stories of other people's suffering. I couldn't get past the first fifty pages of *Demon Camp*, by Jennifer Percy, about PTSD suffered by veterans of war in Iraq and Afghanistan. I don't blame myself, although I do feel guilt. This is the silence that billows up – has billowed up – around my painful memories that others tiptoe around, and that I keep quiet.

I try not to be angry when others turn away. One way of coping with this social blanket of silence is a sort of absurd humour in which I laugh and don't expect anyone else to laugh. I did it when, in a group of writers who decided to go around the circle and share the hilarious stories of losing their virginity, I said, "I was raped." I may have laughed, because I'd ruined the game – at least for that moment. I can't say there wasn't a bit of bitterness to my actions. I did it again when, in that hospital in New Orleans, with my partner and a doctor leaning in to catch my every word, and pneumonia in my chest, I blurted it out – "Rape" – and fell about laughing.

Obviously, it was not funny. I have a vague memory of my partner Chris's face, which was completely solemn and perhaps a bit dismayed, and of the doctor's face, which was also very solemn – probably because the only person who's allowed to crack a smile in this particular situation is the person who has just disclosed the trauma. I laughed until I began to have a coughing fit. I also remember the story of an ill-informed reporter asking Fiona Apple if she had any favourite or worst Thanksgiving experiences and Apple, who was raped around Thanksgiving when she was 12, turning to her sister, off-camera, and bursting out laughing. Sometimes the only way we can bear to react is by filling the silence with laughter, even if we're laughing alone.

Pain is hard for folks to talk about, let alone look straight into the maw of. It's particularly hard if they love you, in which case your wounds may be deeply felt by them as well. This kind of love may look like ignorance, or sound like silence. Sometimes you don't get the response you want, and that creates another wound, a blank space, to carry around with your other ones. You might make jokes about it. Laugh about that, too.

Then you wait for something like pneumonia to come along so that you can tell them that you have pneumonia. You don't have to laugh about pneumonia, which is an infection of one or both of the lungs that inflames the alveoli. People will come around. They'll say, I hope you feel better soon.

And you'll thank them. You will.

A TASTE OF HOME

Our relationship with food is inextricably bound up with the way feel about the people who feed us. **Charlotte Richardson Andrews** looks back at the foods – and people – that have made her who she is today. Art by **Holly Exley**.

Families are such strange things. We inherit them, choose them, marry into and out of them. I think about mine plenty. We're a brilliant, dysfunctional lot – creative, weird, sensitive, ill, magical, empathic, loud and queer. I think about my place in our private matrix and my role in our shared, personal histories. I think about the things that have shaped me, and us, through the years: poverty, strength, trauma, intelligence, abuse, faith, isolation, madness, and love. There are so many ways to understand us, to know and not-know us.

I'm not quite sure how I survived the dark years of my disordered eating during my teens. I didn't tell anyone who could have helped me until years later when the worst of it was over. But somehow, slowly, I healed. I think my girlfriend played a significant part in this mostly subconscious process. In loving her, and allowing her to love me, I was able to dissolve and unlearn my anxieties around my body and food. Eating became a thing we did (and still do) together – enthusiastically and, on my good days, without shame.

Both of my parents have eating disorders. Diet and health are big issues for all of my immediate family. Growing up among that, and my parent's mutual, violent unhappiness – her diet paraphernalia (magazines, eating plans, meal replacement shakes), his glossy high end fashion mags (another story, for another time) – it was kind of a given that I'd inherit and internalise some fucked up ideas.

And yet, when I try to map how we love each other as a family, it's food that flavours my sweetest memories.

73

I think of the Grasmere gingerbread I brought back from the Lake District: sweet, spicy, golden brown ingots baked to a secret recipe; 'green' – the South Asian pestle-crushed paste (garlic, pepper, ginger, salt) that Neena taught me and my mum to make when we lived in the women's refuge, sharing one, big communal kitchen; the dainty, white-icing-and-cherry topped fairy cakes I'd make with my late Nanny Florence (Florrie) in her tidy kitchenette; the rich, powdered-custard trifle my mum makes every Christmas – a sweet, shared proof that we're still here, knitted together, in spite of the complex family legacies we negotiate.

I remember my Auntie Eileen, sadly long gone now, as petite, silver-haired, smiling and anxious. She'd married my Uncle Alan, a West Indian taxi driver, during the '50s. When I was old enough, my mum explained how hard it'd been for them, a working class couple raising mixed race children in Little England. My brother and I used to forage blackberries in her back garden: dark, tart things prickled with fine, fine hairs. Once they'd been rinsed and patted dry, Eileen would serve them back to us on a china saucer with a silver teaspoon, bitter purple juices bleeding into a sweet, plump scoop of frosted milk ice cream.

My granddad wasn't an affectionate man. He'd had a hard life and was consequently, on the surface at least, a hard person. Charismatic but cold. I loved him, despite his indifference. I loved his inky green army tattoos; his old man aftershave; his oak-tree height and his dry wit, which could border on cruel. The first and last time he 'cooked' for me, he made cream crackers. Three golden squares topped with salty white butter and thick slabs of tangy, rich cheddar. I think of him every time I work my way through a packet of Jacob's, one of my go-to comfort foods.

My father and I are semi-estranged. It hurts, acutely, but the distance is necessary. I think of the big, hearty pot stews he'd make when we lived together, after the divorce. A bricolage of bright, deep, roughly chopped greens (peas, kale, garden-grown beans); jagged chunks of potatoes and carrots, sometimes swedes and turnips, too; lentils (green, yellow, red) and pearl barley, all thrown in, simmering away in an earthy, golden stock.

How I see and feel and *do* family life has shifted radically over the last five years. My in-laws, hard-working Portuguese immigrants, are a huge part of that. I knew them at a distance for a long, drawn-out time before they knew me. It took them a while to face who I was, and what I represented: a living, walking reminder that their daughter is queer. But in time, they folded me into their lives, an embrace I am thankful for on a daily basis. We eat together, often – big, traditional roasts my formidable mother-in-law Gloria knocks up on a Sunday, after church. They drop us off dishes too, when they're passing by: home-cooked *caldo verde*; crispy, salty *milho frito*; sweet, lemony *bolo de arroz* fresh from the bakery – one for each of us, *filhas*.

Food that flavours my sweetest memories

"Making the jewellery gives me something to be proud of. They're a symbol of positive change. They give me a window to be able to talk about my recovery to friends and family when I give them as gifts."

"Coming to the knitting group stops me being lonely, I feel so much better after coming to the club. If I finish my knitting at home it stops me dropping off to sleep, and I can watch telly without feeling guilty, I'm not wasting time..."

Birdsong is an ethical fashion company based in London. They are committed to sourcing their products from women's organisations and charities that manufacture ethically and sustainably. We have interviewed women from three of these projects about how the work they do impacts their mental wellbeing. The first of these is Sweet Cavanagh, which produces jewellery designed and made by women in recovery from eating disorders or addiction. The second is a range of knitwear created by the elderly women of the Knit & Natter group in Enfield and the Bradbury Centre in Kingston. The third is Mohila Creations, fashion produced by a group of migrant mothers based in Tower Hamlets. The majority of Birdsong's revenue goes back to community-based initiatives just like these. You can find them at www.birdsong.london

Art by **Sophie Slater**

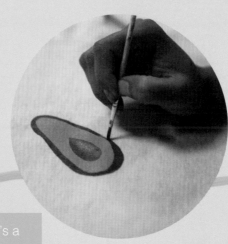

"Painting is so relaxing. It's a big part of who I am now, making the t-shirts and seeing other people like them has really built my confidence."

"...making a piece each week is a wonderful way to soothe and focus my mind. If I'm feeling unmotivated, that's OK too. Perfection didn't need to apply to the jewellery making."

THE COST OF CARE
PART ONE: MAISIE AND SALLY'S STORY

With mental healthcare being hit hard by cuts to the NHS, people living with mental illness are suffering. Mental health services have been stripped back and, in some areas, shut down, leaving vulnerable people with no choice but to move many miles away from home to receive inpatient care. **Ruby Tandoh** looks at the true cost of care for these people, and for the families they leave behind.

Art by **Kaylani McCard**

A night sitter comes to Sally Burke's home some days, watching over her teenage daughter Maisie for a few hours while Sally sleeps. These few snatched hours of rest are all the in-home support she receives. It's a small concession: she needs to sleep, and her daughter needs supervision to ensure that she stays safe, from herself, and from the mental illness that she lives with. You can have what you need to stay alive, the healthcare system seems to say. That, and nothing more.

Mental illness may be common, but it is seldom visible. Sally Burke is a carer and campaigner for mental health awareness, but even anchored so firmly in activism for mental health now, she can remember a time when she rarely had cause to think of the struggle of the mentally unwell. Daughter Maisie had a few play therapy sessions in the aftermath of her parents' separation years ago, but that was as close as the family had come to the sequestered world of mental illness. Sally admits she hadn't even realised that their local children's inpatient unit in Hull had closed down.

When Maisie's behaviour began to worsen, the family were roughly thrust into a world that they'd scarcely knew existed. At age 11, in the aftermath of her father's death,

Maisie began to act in ways that were dangerous to herself and to Sally. She self-harmed, her moods were volatile, and she fell into rages and tantrums that were a far cry from the placidity and sweetness of the little girl that Sally had raised. There were times when Maisie spoke as another persona, Sabrina, and others when she sobbed at the cruelness and hurt that Sabrina represented.

From the luxury of not having needed it, Sally and Maisie had their eyes forcibly opened to the inadequacy of mental health provision in their hometown of Hull. Once, when Maisie was in crisis – at risk of hurting herself and her mum, and in great distress – Sally was forced to call an ambulance in the absence of any other forms of social care or mental health support. Another time, Maisie was taken to an adult mental health ward. "There was very little support for Maisie, and none for myself," Sally explained to me. "There was no out-of-hours professional trained in children's mental health to support us. We had to call an ambulance, who called the police, and these services didn't have a clue what to do. In fact, they were disgusted that no one would help them with this child in great distress. The hospital doctor drugged her to try and calm her down."

There was no out-of-hours professional trained in children's mental health to support us. We had to call an ambulance, who called the police, and these services didn't have a clue what to do.

This wasn't the only time that Maisie and Sally were left floundering. The family was followed for a spell by filmmakers for a Channel 4 documentary series called *Kids On The Edge*. The series took an unflinching look at some of the most urgent social and emotional dilemmas facing young people today. When it came to Maisie's story, the issue in question was the mental health of girls, and the ways that the underfunded system lets them down.

Watch the episode, called *Troubled Girls*, and you can see first-hand the isolation dealt to Sally and Maisie. It's not just a result of the stigma attached to Maisie's volatile and often self-destructive mental illness. It's because of the healthcare system, and the way it seems intent on snatching away even their last vestiges of togetherness. Due to underfunding and a lack of services in East Yorkshire, Maisie was wrenched away from her mum and placed in a psychiatric facility almost 100 miles away in Bury, close to Manchester. Mother and daughter were forced to survive for weeks apart, at the height of Maisie's vulnerability. It's impossible to ignore the sense that this hurts mum Sally just as keenly as it strikes Maisie.

These periods of separation are interspersed with times of relative calm, when Maisie's health is better, and Sally is able to meet most of her caring needs within the sanctuary of the family home. And yet even with Maisie now attending a non-mainstream school which can better accommodate her and her needs, there's still a lot that Sally is fighting for. "Everything with education has taken a very long time. They don't understand mental health and they have no placements with trained staff for such children."

"There needs to be flexible community care that caters to the individual child's needs," Sally explains. "We literally have no resources in the East Riding. It really is a postcode lottery." She shares a resource wishlist that includes a local crisis unit, art and music therapies, autism support and family workshops. She campaigns for much of this through The Maisie Project – an initiative run in partnership with SANE, a leading UK mental health charity – aiming to establish a network of community care for mental illness in East Yorkshire and beyond. It's a push back against the cuts that have repeatedly struck Child and Adolescent Mental Health Services, and a crusade to help the vulnerable young people, and their carers, who suffer as a result.

In spite of losing her teaching job and home in the fight to secure care for Maisie, Sally continues to devote herself to advocacy and campaigning for the rights of her child, and others like her, wherever possible. There can be no justice for the mentally ill until there is support for those who love and care for them. With each hurdle that Sally clears in order to receive the paltry £62-a-week carer's allowance that she is entitled to, Maisie suffers a little more. Every moment that Sally spends fighting to retain access to her counselling sessions – which are invaluable in balancing the emotional toll of caring for such a profoundly ill young person – is a moment lost. Faced with neglect, indifference and even hostility from all sides of the health establishment, Sally has been let down. And when we let Sally down, we let Maisie down, too.

"I have had to fight this system relentlessly," Sally wrote to us. These are battles that she fights every day just to achieve a minimal level of support from the state for her and her child. Each day calls for renewed strength: to fight for representation, for education, for the provision of facilities and even for the right to sleep safe in the knowledge that her sick daughter is being watched over. These hard-fought-for nights are fitful while there is still work to be done. Sally echoes herself just a few lines later in her email, a note of frustration piercing her words: "I have had to fight this system relentlessly!"

A percentage of the proceeds from the sales of this magazine will be donated directly to Sally Burke and Maisie, to help with the costs of a much-needed holiday.

THE COST OF CARE
PART TWO: ABI'S STORY

At the height of her struggle with anorexia, Abigale Feasey was put in an inpatient unit for people with eating disorders, hundreds of miles from her family home in Teesside. What does it mean for eating disorder recovery when the life you're trying to return to is so far away? Words by **Ruby Tandoh**. Art by **Grace Helmer**.

Abigale Feasey was a recovered anorexic. Or at least, she was a recovered anorexic in the eyes of the doctors and nurses of the health service. It's in these people's hands – in their degrees and their science, in their method and meticulousness and maths – that we place our trust when it comes to health. Having been an outpatient attending regular sessions with a dietitian and specialist nurse for two years, Abigale was told that she was well enough to be discharged from their care. Her BMI was higher, and so she was well. In spite of the anxieties that continued to plague her relationship with food,

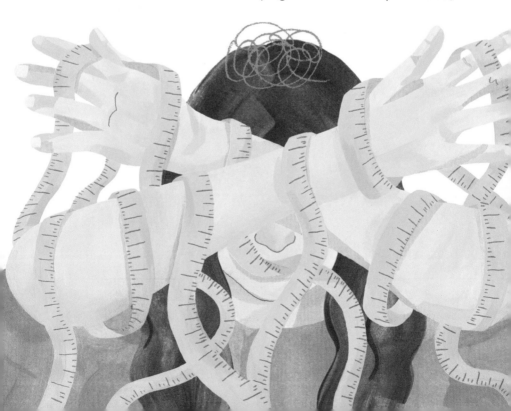

Abigale trusted the professionals. Her BMI was up, after all, and that little number on the page, wavering a decimal point or two above the thin red line, was all that mattered.

Then, in the summer following her second year at university, Abigale's mental health quickly deteriorated again. Unable to continue with her English degree, she withdrew from her studies, and with no available beds on a specialist eating disorder ward anywhere in the UK, she was checked into a ward in a general mental health facility. She was housed with women whose mental illnesses ranged from schizophrenia to paranoia. With so little space to accommodate such a broad range of mental health problems, these very different illnesses curdled together, Abi's anorexia left free to bloom as she compulsively walked the corridors of the hospital, the cries of the other patients hanging in the air.

Abi paced the halls to burn calories, and barely ate a thing. "The staff there didn't understand my illness at all and would never intervene," she explained to me in our emails. "My family were absolutely traumatised, watching me slowly die in a hospital environment." Her weight continued to drop, and she was at risk of self-harm and even suicide.

Abi was transferred to a local NHS hospital medical ward. Still unable to eat properly, she was threatened with the prospect of being sectioned. By this point, Abi was at the most critical level of risk for a person with an eating disorder. It was decided that, in the absence of any spare NHS beds in eating disorder units, she would have to be moved to London, some 250 miles away from her home and family, in order to seek treatment on a private ward there. The bed was paid for by the NHS commissioning body, but the costs of such inaccessible care were far greater than just the financial implications.

"It was a traumatic experience," Abi told me. "I had never been away from home for a long period of time before. I have three siblings, who I'm very close to, so being away from them was awful. I think i resented the hospital in London. I hated the fact they were so strict and I was so far away from home. I wanted to rebel against their treatment." Away from friends and family, Abi found it hard to reconcile the progress that she had made on the ward with the reality of life in the 'real world' outside. "It didn't feel real because I was so far away from home, so I couldn't apply the skills they were trying to teach me to my life. Although they managed to increase my BMI in that three-month period, mentally I was just the same, if not worse."

Eventually, Abi was transferred to an inpatient unit closer to home, but her recovery was slow there, and she was forcibly kept in care for her own good. After a long thirteen months, she was deemed well enough – and her BMI high enough – to make her own decisions about her care, and she soon discharged herself from the unit, keen to be back home with her family. Although she still lived with the daily torment of her eating disorder, she stepped free from inpatient care.

With a personal history so fraught with anxiety and mental ill health, it's tempting to characterise Abi's life as a tragic one. We're taught that some people are just 'troubled' – that this is part of who they are, not what they feel. In this view of mental illness, the person and the illness are one and the same thing. Even if you recover, you are still ill at heart. Even if you slip in and out of mental health problems, it's the periods of sickness that define who you are. But Abi is defying that narrative.

In spite of the illness she suffered and the difficult, lengthy, isolating care that she received, Abi is stepping forward. She's now back at university, finishing her final year and hoping to move to London to pursue a career as a journalist. She has resources that help her in her recovery and dreams for the future. Having tumbled from hospital bed to hospital bed, however, she sees room for improvement in the health system that treated her: "I think that GPs need training in eating disorders. There need to be a lot more specialist eating disorder units and beds. There needs to be awareness [of mental health] from an early age."

She also has big doubts about the little number that has been the barometer of her illness, the number that had her admitted to wards and discharged from care. Considering the nightmare experience that Abi had within the health system, you'd be forgiven for thinking that she would be grateful for the BMI number that has now risen enough, just enough, for her to break away from that system, from illness, into 'health' in the outside world. She's sceptical. "The whole BMI guidelines need to be re-evaluated. It's not just about what your BMI is, it's to do with what's going on inside your head." She tells us about her dreams of living life, having fun, laughing and dancing. This isn't a health that you can measure in numbers.

ACTING QUEER

We all like to see people like us on screen. We feel the pull towards films with plots that run parallel to our own, with characters in whose footsteps we can follow. Because the world of cinema is so huge and so reliant on capital, and privileged structures of promotion and distribution, films don't always show us stories as diverse as the people who watch them, though. Dominant narratives tend to be white, straight, cisgender and good-looking, and many of us don't see ourselves on screen until the film credits have finished and we glimpse ourselves dim and hazy in the black mirror of the dormant TV.

Queer people are wildly underrepresented on screen; so too are mentally unwell people. And yet at the intersection of queer and mentally ill, we find a set of thriving cinema stereotypes that resurface time and time again, across eras, genres and styles. The trope of the 'crazy queer' is one that sits just as central to cinematic history as the gutsy ingenue or the misunderstood-but-valiant outsider nerd. It's a warping of our experiences, and one that seldom does justice to the realities of what it is to be a mentally ill person in the LGBTQ community. Here's an illustrated taxonomy of mentally ill queer (or queer-coded) characters on screen – the good, the bad and the ugly.

Words by **Ruby Tandoh**
Art by **Kelsey Wroten**

Femmes Fatales

I was giddy with excitement when I first saw **Cruel Intentions**, and of course I lingered longer than I maybe should have done on the scene where Sarah Michelle Gellar's scheming, sociopathic Kathryn seduces hapless ingenue Cecile. This luxuriant, amoral, wicked world of rich New York teens, interrupted with flashes of queerness, was everything that was supposed to be awful with the world. I loved it.

This trope of single-mindedly dastardly queer women is one that reaches its gnarly fingers out far beyond just sexy teen dramas, though. Look at Peter Jackson's 1994 psychological thriller **Heavenly Creatures**, where Kate Winslet and Melanie Lynskey's intense, queer-coded friendship leads them to cold-blooded murder, in a reimagining of an infamous real-life crime. **Monster** also draws inspiration from true crime in its portrayal of serial killer Aileen Wuornos, showing the mental illness and trauma that sent Aileen spiralling towards fatal brutality.

If *Monster* is a film that hints at the humanity of its subject, then **Basic Instinct** provides the blueprint for the exact opposite: the queer woman murderer, whose coded psychopathy manifests as a kind of seductive *femme fatale* caricature. While Sharon Stone's character famously wears no pants in one notorious scene, her on-screen girlfriend represents a different kind of queerness: the aggressive, gutsy foil to Stone's sex-led slyness. Their relationship is tempestuous; their sexuality is fraught. Predictably, it's men who suffer their wrath.

But don't give up on your crime-filled queer dreams just yet! In queer classic **Bound**, we see a heartier alternative to these stereotypes. Directed by the transgender Wachowski sisters (who went on to direct *The Matrix* trilogy), it's a sultry neo-noir thriller that puts a same-gender relationship at the heart of an organised crime storyline. Though their conniving is framed as a kind of sociopathy, the women's personalities are rich and vibrant and full. **Set It Off** is another great example of this, with Queen Latifah's bolshy and brilliant Cleo going to show that butch queer women can channel a very masculine anger, while having kind hearts, great minds and good friends. Watch and learn.

High-Camp Villainy

It's not always easy to look evil in the eye. In lots of films, particularly children's films, this means subverting the straightforward concept of aggression, and casting villainous characters in a slightly different, less intimidating light. This means stripping away macho violence, and bringing in a glitzy, glam, unconscionably evil camp villain.

Take Scar, for instance – Simba's cruel uncle and wannabe ruler in **The Lion King**. His lilting drawl, effete mannerisms and cowardliness are all ways of hinting at queerness. Conveniently, these traits position Scar as a complete negation of the hyper-masculine stolidity that Mufasa embodies. Scar is weak and angular, Mufasa is broad and brave; Scar is caught up in narcissistic, ritualistic excess, Mufasa is a martyr.

Look at Jafar, too, in 1992 Disney classic **Aladdin** and even, more recently, Tamatoa, the villainous crab in last year's hit film **Moana**. To a Lin-Manuel Miranda soundtrack, Tamatoa spins exuberantly around his lair, the treasure encrusting his back sparkling like a giant disco ball as he sings and waltzes into the camp villain history books.

Watch **Rocky Horror Picture Show**, however, and you can find a clever play on these age-old ideas. This isn't a queer-coded villain in a heterosexual world: instead, two supposedly heterosexual victims are thrust into a raucous, fantastical, evil world of queer debauchery. It's as camp as camp can be, and it's these openly queer villains in charge.

LGBTD
(Lesbian, Gay, Bisexual and Transgender Depression)

"I just don't want your life to be any harder than it has to be." This is something that countless queer people will have heard in response to their coming out, often from the people closest to them. Contained in this cliché is the assumption of a tragic narrative: to be queer is to be sad, and if you can avoid it, you should. It's little surprise that misguided friends and family take this approach when so many of the stories we're fed about queerness are ones that centre depression and mental ill health.

Even in **Little Miss Sunshine**, which is by all accounts a perky and optimistic look at being an outsider in a pristine world, we see this kind of storyline unfold. One outsider is Dwayne, whose existential teen angst leads him to a self-punishing vow of silence, and then there's Olive, whose pot-belly and speccy awkwardness leaves her on the fringes of the beauty pageant world. But most memorable, for me, is Frank, the depressed gay uncle and Proust scholar, whose bandaged wrists point to his suicidal dejection, and whose gayness is at the heart of that melancholy.

In **A Single Man**, depression again takes centre stage, with a day in the life of Colin Firth's abjectly sad George, a middle-aged college professor whose partner died less than a year before. Drifting through his day, furnished by director Tom Ford in a sumptuous mixture of aestheticism and sadness, he sinks helplessly into the past, pushes hard against those around him and struggles to confront the reality of his pain. As is the trajectory of so many queer films, even in his moment of clarity, George's story flies inexorably towards tragedy.

Not all films that depict mentally ill queer characters make an effort to illuminate the ways in which a homophobic society – not queerness itself – might be responsible for catalysing and reinforcing these mental health problems. **Show Me Love** (also known as *Fucking Åmål*) is a Swedish film that goes some way towards remedying this deficit. A gentle, ambling exploration of the lives of two queer teen girls in small-town Sweden, it hints at the ways that Agnes's depression and self-harm might be traced back to the isolation and anxiety she feels as a bullied, not-yet-out young person.

Psycho(path)

Transgender people have a long and troublesome history of their lives being instrumentalised to represent 'craziness' on film. Before transgender rights and realities had begun to gain traction in the mainstream, Alfred Hitchcock's 1960 horror classic, **Psycho**, set the tone. Norman Bates is the film's eponymous psycho, with his cross-dressing and his predatoriness portrayed as two sides of the same psychopathy. We are supposed to fear him not so much because of what he's capable of, but what he is: a person split along lines of gender and sanity, and whose inner ugliness leaks out of all the cracks in between.

The Silence of The Lambs picks up where *Psycho* left off, when it comes to transgender identities being used as a shorthand for insanity. Here the link between transgender lives and violence is drawn even more explicitly, though, with the film's elusive serial killer fashioning a kind of 'suit' out of the skin of their female victims. This violence is a surrogate for the formal sex reassignment surgery denied to Buffalo Bill some years prior. There's no equivocation between gender transition and violence: transgender lives mean surgery, and surgery is butchery, we're told.

It's not just transgender people who have had their identities made symbols for madness. To drift into the world of TV for a moment, take a look at Willow's journey from sweetness to unmitigated evil in **Buffy the Vampire Slayer**, conveniently concurrent with her burgeoning queerness. Something similar happens in **Black Swan**, too, as darkness ripples around Natalie Portman's troubled Nina and her bisexuality blooms.

In **The Talented Mr Ripley**, this trope reaches a dazzlingly violent and seductive peak, with Matt Damon's portrayal of cold-blooded killer and pathological liar, Tom Ripley. Tom's coded homosexuality isn't just incidental to his cruelness: it's precisely his obsession with Dickie Greenleaf that leads him to descend so abruptly into madness. It's a film ripe with queer romance and erotic tension, all teetering on the knife edge of Tom's waning sanity.

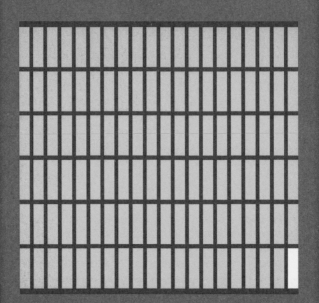

In 2016, **119** prisoners took their lives. **Suicide has risen dramatically** in the last three years.

HEALTH BEHIND BARS

Prisoners suffer mental health problems at rates far higher than among the general population, and incidents of suicide in custody are on the rise. How can we do better? Words and art by **Ruby Tandoh**.

66% of prisoners have a **personality disorder**

Depression and anxiety are over **3 times** more common among prisoners

Those in prison are 8 times more likely to suffer from psychosis than the general population

Self-harm among prisoners has increased by **26%**

Because prison is viewed, and run, as a punitive operation in the UK, we give little thought to what happens to the people we lock away. There's a sense that prison, in its capacity as a deterrent to crime, should be as punishing as possible, and that standards for wellbeing should be limited.It's not easy to avoid sensationalist stories of prisoners with flat screen televisions, games consoles and other 'luxuries' in their cells, as though these distractions could ever provide any real mitigating comfort against a total loss of personal freedom. This mindset, coupled with the intense strain that the criminal justice system is under, leaves little room for a culture of caring within the prison system.

The lack of appropriate mental healthcare within prisons is just one of the issues that this has led to, and it's something that the Centre for Mental Health (CMH) has researched extensively. In a recent report, they referenced the some 90% of prisoners who live with a mental health problem, personality disorder or substance misuse problem. This points to a huge crisis of mental health within the criminal justice system, whereby the most vulnerable within society are being imprisoned en masse, and the prison system itself at best fails to treat, at worst exacerbates, the mental health problems of those in custody.

CMH gives several hypotheses about the roots of this crisis. One finding was the inadequacy of mental health training among prison staff, another pointed to the impact of financial cuts that left prisons understaffed and unable to provide escorts for prisoners' appointments, counselling sessions and so on. Crucially, there is a fundamental misunderstanding of mental health among many of the professionals and prisoners within the system. The complex ways that mental health problems may manifest in a person – a person out of their home environment, in confinement and without the usual dreams and diversions of everyday life – are poorly understood, and this leads to a culture where these symptoms are taken as manipulative, aggressive, deliberately confrontational or uncooperative. What ought to be read as signs of need and vulnerability are instead further criminalised, leading to a cycle of distrust, abuse and self-harm.

What's more, when prisoners eventually leave custody, they not only return to the 'real world' with their mental health potentially worse than ever, but they risk homelessness following release, poor job prospects and poverty. This is a system that neglects some of the most deprived

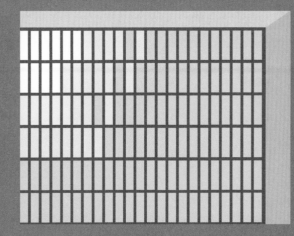

communities in our country, criminalises their survival mechanisms, and pathologises their reactions to hardship. The solution? The road forward will need us to completely overhaul our understanding of what justice looks like, and what a criminal deserves. As put in the Centre for Mental Health's report: "We need a profound culture shift in prisons from a primarily punitive approach, to one centred around recovery, wellbeing and rehabilitation."

Quotes and statistics from the *Preventing Prison Suicide* briefing by the Howard League for Penal Reform and the Centre for Mental Health, and *Mental Health and Criminal Justice* – a report by the Centre for Mental Health.

HANG ON TO THE NIGHT

Sara Quin is one half of pop duo Tegan and Sara, and co-founder of LGBTQ charity the Tegan and Sara Foundation. She talked to music journalist **Laura Snapes** about double standards, anxiety attacks and the importance of being vulnerable.

Art by **Ha Gyung Lee** and **Kate Rado**

I thought maybe a good point to start would be *Hang on to the Night* [a song from Tegan and Sara's latest album, *Love You to Death*]. Who are you singing to?

I think that whenever I write something, it's always to myself. Our grandfather died in the middle of us making *Love You to Death*. It was suicide; it was really jarring. He had lived a really good life and he was in his nineties and I sort of have an admiration for someone who takes agency over their life, especially when they're not well and they're struggling – I feel like an advocate for not attaching stigma or shame to it. But then, on the other hand, it's tough when it's someone you love.

With creativity in general, do you find writing through trauma to be a cathartic process, or are you blocked when you're not feeling at your best?

In the periods of our career when I've been depressed or really struggling, I'm definitely not productive. That's not my zone at all. I usually find that my areas of productivity are right before something bad happens [laughs]. Like almost a weird foreshadowing. So much of what we wrote for our 2007 album, *The Con*, Tegan was going through intense relationship stuff and I was thinking, "I'm in a great place!" and then my grandmother died and someone who was working with the band who we were really close to died and all of a sudden my relationship died, and I thought, "Fuck". All of the music that I had been writing during what I thought was a really good time, I think seemed appropriately in line with the next couple of years, which were so bad and so hard.

Have you found support from within the industry when you've been feeling depressed or under pressure? The music industry has a terrible reputation for helping musicians with mental health issues.

I think Tegan and I have been really purposeful in not blurring the line of personal and professional, but it does make it complicated when what's happening in your personal life so deeply impacts what's happening in your professional life. There have been times where

I've thought, "Oh my god, I can't believe we'll be pushed to do these things when it's so obvious that we're near collapse." But then isn't it my job to tell people? I don't know if that's passing the responsibility back to myself, though. I mean, if we're not well we're not well, but it's definitely not something that I feel like we've always been good at dealing with.

When Tegan and I were at our worst, in terms of our relationship with each other, that was the first time in our career we actually cancelled shows. One of my managers was very angry with us, because in his mind we were probably behaving the way we always behaved. Knowing now the scope of what was happening, he would never have had that response. But at that time, we felt like we'd let everyone down. We thought, we can never cancel a show again. Now we've learned how to talk about the pain we're in and how bad things are, I think there's more sensitivity, but it's an ongoing challenge.

You brought up something that I think is really important – not wanting to seem vulnerable. As figureheads for the LGBTQ community, which is so often underrepresented, have you felt like you've had to always put across a really strong front, and not show the cracks?

Oh god yeah. Some of it is probably our upbringing – we didn't see our parents be vulnerable. Our mum is a single parent. She didn't take sick days. She was going to school and working and raising us, and my dad is a notorious workaholic, he works six and a half days a week. We basically have to beg him whenever he needs to go to the doctor. So there was not a lot of 'weakness' shown in my family. When we started out with our music career it felt like there were not really a lot of safe people or safe spaces for us. I think that our reaction was to buffer ourselves from all of that and be early for everything and to do the job better than anybody else would do it and to never ask for anything extra. Don't be demanding. Don't be high maintenance.

I think we maybe ruffled feathers twice in our entire career and it was so obvious how extreme the fallout was. In 2006 or 2007, I forget now, we did a radio event in Chicago and we didn't realise that one of the microphones was on. We were setting up and soundchecking

and Tegan and I had a private conversation – what we thought was a private conversation – about how we didn't want to do the event and how it was stupid, and how it was in a Subway shop, with a meatball... It was degrading to me to be the entertainment for the lunchtime rush and I didn't understand why we were doing it. Someone at the station overheard us and the programme director has not played our music for ten years. We've gone back and pitched many other singles and he is very clear that until we apologise, we will never be played on his radio station. And we won't apologise. I don't feel proud of the fact that they heard us have that conversation, but I feel like I have to stand up for us. I do feel that there is a double standard for women, and I know it's not a popular thing to talk about but I do think that women are expected to look and act a certain way. I've literally seen men trash dressing rooms, fight, scream, not show up to things, or say they hate radio stations. Often with men, it's not even considered a thing.

There is totally that trope of the shambolic, depressed musician, which is only ever romanticised for men. There was this amazing Pitchfork article about the "gendering of martyrdom", about how Kurt Cobain is revered as this romantic poet whereas Amy Winehouse was seen as a pitiful mess.

Tegan and I are more serious artists than a lot of people have ever given us credit for. I think when you're a woman and you're writing about things that are emotional – feelings or relationships or whatever – people find it really easy to write the music off. We still struggle with that sort of double standard. I see it all the time – there are male lyricists out there where I'm just like, how is this music 'genius'? Or how is this music 'profound'? Then I listen to certain female artists and I think like, oh my god, this is like fucking PhD compared to that. But people are like, you know, "Isn't that cute?" That is problematic. I don't want to be forced to take ourselves so seriously and really hammer it home, like, here we are not having fun! Proving how serious we are! Because at the end of the day, music is still a release for us. It's something incredibly powerful and cathartic, in an almost like down-to-your-nervous-system kind of way. I think that's profound. I definitely walk that fine line of wanting us to be 'serious' and talk about the things that matter to us while also not being a goddamn misery for people to listen to.

You both said recently that to be strong leaders, in general and for the Tegan and Sara Foundation, you need to be healthy and confident. What does mental health and wellbeing look like for you? What do you do to take care of yourself?

I'm one of those people who doesn't do anything that I should be doing. My mom is a therapist and she'll be like, "You should meditate!" I don't do any of it. I don't even pretend. I don't know why. I'm an incredibly organised, disciplined person, when it comes to everything that isn't me or my body. I've never been very good at regular exercise – I go through periods of being incredibly healthy and then I'll go through periods of what, to me, is very unhealthy. I'm not shooting drugs and putting myself in high risk situations or whatever, or eating a pepperoni pizza for every single meal – but by my own body and emotional standards, I don't always take care of myself. But then I'll have other stretches of time, like last year, where I worked out with a trainer and I was like, "I'm a machine!!!!!! No one can stop me, I'm in the best health of my liiiife!!!" I was eating well and I was sleeping well and I was doing all these great things. And then we start touring again and I eat too much, drink too much, I don't go to the gym, I'm completely stressed out, I wake up in cold sweats with anxiety attacks.

You're also a big news junkie. Have you been managing that line between being informed and being overwhelmed in the current climate? I don't know how anybody does.

[Laughs] I admire and envy people who are sort of checked out. I actually feel like I've turned a corner in the last couple of weeks. I was probably not even acknowledging how truly upset I felt about what's happening in the United States. I think some little kid that lives inside of me was freaking out, like, "Oh my God, is the world going to end? I need somebody to tell me it's going to be OK." I don't necessarily feel like I have that person in my life, so I've been in this cycle of quiet resignation. Like, this is it. It's all over. We're fucked. I think that what's particularly taxing about it is that we are public figures and so we're expected to, I don't know man, I can't just write in caps on Twitter "WE'RE ALL GONNA DIE!!!!!" I think about it, I think about saying what I *really* think all the time, but I don't know how effective or helpful that will be for anyone but me.

But I do think I've turned a bit of a corner and I'm doing a little bit better and part of that is the [Tegan and Sara] Foundation and being able to physically *do* something. I just want to feel helpful. I want to feel like I'm really doing something. When I'm too much in my head and just reading things or tweeting things, I actually feel insane.

I was going to ask you whether you had worked specifically with any mental health charities with the Foundation. But I also figured mental health is literally at the heart of every single thing you're doing, because not being able to find healthcare or employment opportunities or share your rights with your partner, all those things have enormous mental health ramifications.

We often don't get the full treatment or the support that we need. On a personal level, I know that's true of myself. When I was a kid, I thought I was sick all the time. I spent from fourth grade until about sixth grade fanatically obsessed with the idea that I had cancer. To the point where finally my paediatrician allowed me to get testing done and ultrasounds and actually proved to me that I wasn't sick. As an adult, in therapy, I figured out that this was my way of telling the adults in my life that I was stressed out. I didn't have stomach cancer, but I did have, like, emotional cancer.

We live in a world where we are expected to advocate for ourselves and get the things that we need. What if you can't? What if you don't have those skills? What if you didn't have a mom who kicked down your door and demanded to know what was going on with you? What if you are isolated socially and emotionally and physically from getting the help that you need? I think that by servicing our own LGBTQ community we can help with that. I don't think of the Foundation like it's only going to help LGBTQ women. I think When you strengthen

"We want to help another generation of [LGBTQ] kids into fields that need that: need our voices, need our empathy and need our unique experiences."

some of these institutions or develop programmes that benefit people who are often ignored or forgotten, it ends up helping everybody.

Do you have a twelve-month view – like concrete things that you'd really like to see enacted in the first year of the Foundation?

I look at this as something that might be ongoing throughout our lives. This recent U.S. election emphasises that. If our agency, safety, health and wellbeing can be so drastically changed by an administration change, we're going to have to be vigilant. I think that it's not something you can fix or solve or change permanently. But I do feel hopeful that whatever we do and whatever we're able to achieve, if we can do it *now* – if this is the hardest time to do it – then hopefully we're moving towards a time where it will be easier.

We're also looking at doing stuff with the Foundation that shows how many amazing things are happening – how many victories there have been, and the strength within the LGBTQ community. We want to help another generation of kids into fields that need that: need our voices, need our empathy and need our unique experiences. Specifically in areas around technology and in healthcare. It's important to recognise that we're not just talking about gaining access to these services, but putting people into positions of power within those services. So we have people from our communities who are representing us.

Thank you so much for being so open with us.

I wouldn't necessarily be oversharing so much if it were for a music article. I wouldn't be so forthcoming. But I think it's such an important thing for people in visible positions to talk about mental health, because that's the thing I hear over and over again – especially from our fans. They really do imagine sometimes that they're the only one who's having these problems, and that somehow success or power would fix this stuff. But I think a lot of people everywhere struggle with this stuff. No matter what position of power, or lack of power, you're in. I hope this is a helpful contribution.

This interview has been edited and abridged for clarity.

Find the Tegan and Sara Foundation at
www.teganandsarafoundation.org

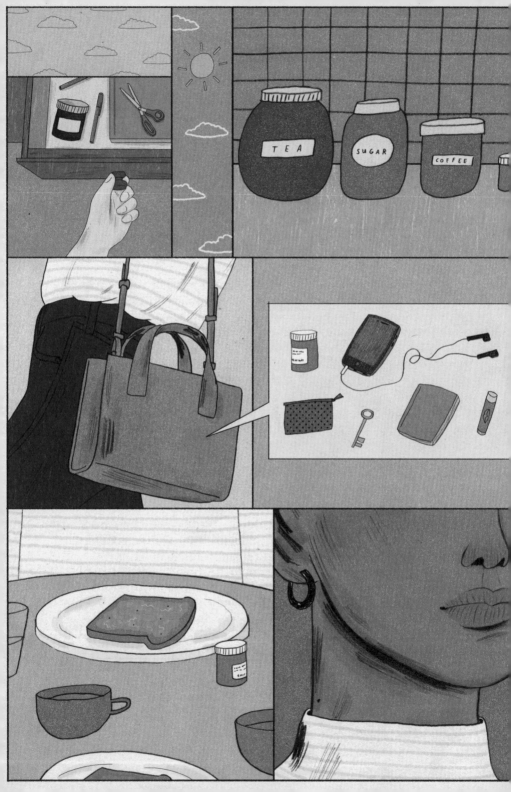

SWEETEN THE PILL

How do you navigate mental health medication in a world that judges you for seeking help? **Becky Appleton** separates the truth from the taboo.

Art by **Manjit Thapp**

Whether it's furtively hiding a packet of pills at the bottom of your bag, worrying about burdening family and friends, or lying to your boss about the real reason you're not in work today, we tend to hide any evidence of problems we have with our mental health. Mainstream media can exacerbate the stereotypes that paint people with mental illnesses as dangerous or violent; these stereotypes feed the stigma that mentally ill people face. This can have a detrimental effect on sufferers and delay people accessing the correct treatment. One particularly stigmatised treatment is medication, which to many is seen as some sort of admission of guilt, or a sign that you've reached rock bottom.

Drug treatments are one of the most common types of therapy for mental health conditions. Some people use medication alone to help them manage their symptoms, while others use it in conjunction with other courses of treatment such as talking therapies. Prescribed medications are often used to treat symptoms of depression, anxiety or psychosis, or as a mood stabiliser for people suffering from a condition such as bipolar disorder.

Antidepressants are a class of drug which can treat various disorders, not just depression. They work by increasing levels of certain chemicals in our brain known as neurotransmitters. One neurotransmitter typically targeted by these drugs is serotonin, a chemical linked to improved mood. Selective Serotonin Re-uptake Inhibitors (SSRIs) act to stop serotonin being reabsorbed at the synapses in our brain, therefore increasing its overall levels and reducing the symptoms of the illness.

However, just because medication which increases the levels of neurotransmitters in our brains can help relieve our symptoms, it doesn't mean that all mental illness is necessarily caused by a lack of these chemicals in the first place. The onset of mental illness is more complex, and often involves an interaction of lifestyle, environmental and biological factors. To put it simply: taking paracetamol helps to relieve the symptoms of a headache, but that doesn't mean the headache was caused by a lack of paracetamol!

The use of medication to treat mental illness is on the rise, with the number of prescriptions for antidepressants more than doubling between 2005 and 2015. However, despite this increase, stigma still remains around taking medication. It's often kept secret, as if something to be ashamed of. It shouldn't be this way. If you're taking medication to manage symptoms of mental illness, then this simply shows you're taking steps to get better. People happily take medication for physical aches and pains, and our mental strains should be no different. For some, a spell of treatment can help them into remission, while for others, medication will be a lifelong way of mitigating the symptoms of a long-term mental illness.

As with many drugs, it's important to be mindful of possible side effects and to seek the guidance, where you can, of a GP. Most side effects pass within a month or so, but some may last for a longer period of time. If you're currently taking some medication for your mental health and experiencing unpleasant side effects then you don't need to suffer in silence – you can go back to your psychiatrist or GP. There may be a different type of medication which could work better for you. Equally, if you would like to get treatment for a mental illness but don't want to take medication at all, then that's fine too! Your GP should be able to discuss other options with you.

Of course medication doesn't just have to mean prescribed drugs. Self-medicating through recreational drugs or alcohol to manage the symptoms of a mental illness is common. Some people find this a useful way of regulating mood, away from the judgement or bureaucracy of the health system. Unfortunately, though, these are often short-term solutions which aren't always what's best for our mental health in the long run. It's important to bear this in mind. There is also a trend for ordering drugs from online pharmacies to avoid having to contact a GP and get a prescription, despite the risks associated with buying from unlicensed vendors. You have no guarantees that the medication you order is right for you, or even that it's what it claims to be at all.

What should you do if you're struggling and would like to be prescribed medication as part of your treatment? The first step is to talk to a healthcare professional who should be able to give you reliable advice on whether medication could work for you. If you don't feel comfortable raising this with your GP then there are other places you could go for help, such as community mental health centres and charities such as Mind.

If you're taking medication for a mental illness, remember that you are not alone. It doesn't have to be kept secret, and it's nothing to be ashamed of.

THE CORNERSTONE

A few months after starting therapy at the Cornerstone in Sheffield, **Leah Pritchard** interviews one of its co-owners, Gail Evans, to talk about counselling's benefits, and its limitations. Art by **Jessamy Hawke**.

On the corner of a residential street just outside of Sheffield city centre, you'll find the Cornerstone. In this ordinary semi-detached house, there are five therapy rooms, and in each room two or three chairs, a small table with maybe a lamp, a pile of felt tips or a box of tissues. There might be a plant in the corner or a couple of paintings hanging on the wall. In the small waiting room downstairs, there's a sign telling you to help yourself to tea or water in the adjoining kitchen. The radio is always on and the counsellors wait in the room next door, not talking in muffled businesslike tones, but chatting, laughing, catching up.

I knew all this from the multiple interrogations I'd subjected my girlfriend, Ruby, to, as

she'd started going to the Cornerstone for counselling a few weeks before I did. Yet even with the knowledge that this place, and the people working there, were as welcoming as I could imagine, I still couldn't help my nerves. I hovered around the front door for ten minutes before my first session. I shuffled in my seat as other people entered the waiting room. I texted Ruby at 6:55 *"Do you think she's forgotten me?" "No, she'll get you at 7"*. Of course, she did.

Several months after my nerve-wracking first session, I interviewed Gail Evans, co-owner of the Cornerstone, for this magazine. I told Gail about my urge to bolt when I had sat in that waiting room for the first time, and she was unsurprised. "It takes a lot of courage to go to therapy. You're going to open up something that's very private, that the chances are you don't speak to anybody about. The prospect of going and knocking on a door and standing there and waiting for this person, when you have no idea what they're going to be like, is terrifying."

For many years, I went through cycles of being depressed, feeling too bad to even consider what help I might need, to feeling good, optimistic and seemingly able to cope on my own. There's this idea, which I bought into, that

you need to be really unwell to go to therapy, or else risk being put down as some kind of fraud. "A lot of people say 'I don't really know why I'm here, I just don't feel right'. That's good enough," says Gail.

On top of that, there are all of the preconceptions you have about what counselling might entail. Surely it's going to be excruciatingly awkward and intrusive and uncomfortable? What if I have nothing to say? Or, on the flipside: how on earth are they going to make me feel better when there's so much that I'm anxious about? "People often think, 'I'm mad, bad or stupid to have this problem'," says Gail. "What they learn is that it's very normal to have these problems, and it doesn't mean that you're weak. In a non-judging atmosphere, most often, people find their own solutions to things. By and large, people just need to be held and supported while they access their own strength and knowledge about themselves."

"A lot of people say 'I don't really know why I'm here, I just don't feel right'. That's good enough."

It's strange to think that conversations with a person who doesn't know you could help you to better understand yourself. But so often you do just need that professional hand to help you hold back your inner critic – those feelings that you're "mad, bad or stupid" – for long enough to get a glimpse at what your feelings, emotions and dreams really are. If we can learn to quiet that inner critic with our counsellor's help, we can learn to do it for ourselves. With time, hopefully, we can reduce it to a murmur, and then to silence.

***

Not everyone will find salvation in the counsellor's chair, though. In a society where certain groups are marginalised, income is wildly skewed and politics polarised, some mental health problems need a bigger intervention. A few years ago, after referral by my GP, I went to a series of group classes in Cognitive Behavioural Therapy (a popular talking treatment available on the NHS, which focuses on how your thoughts, beliefs and attitudes affect your feelings and behaviour). For me, these were helpful – I think even the act of going, and showing myself I was worth caring for, was enough to drag me out of my rut at the time. But there was a woman there who raised her hand in every session to ask how the tutor could help her with her debt, with her problems with immigration, and with her family, who were terrified. She was referred to the classes because she desperately needed help – help with her mental wellbeing, sure – but a CBT class could never relieve her of the pressures that made her head so heavy every day.

Though there are many legitimate reasons people avoid going to their GP, many of us – just like the woman from my class – will turn to them if we're having what we perceive to be mental health difficulties. One of the problems with this, Gail says, is that "[they] might be diagnosing something as a mental health difficulty when it might actually be a social difficulty, or a societal difficulty. There have been a number of times when I've said to a client, I think you need to be seeing your MP. How can you be focussing on this when you don't know where your next meal is coming from, or if you're getting your housing benefit next week?" No doubt the symptoms of poverty, or of fielding racist or anti-immigrant microaggressions, can look a lot like symptoms of mental illness.

Systems of oppression affect everything in counselling, just as they do in broader society. Who can access therapy? Often it's those with money, with supportive family or friends, who won't be endangered by admitting to mental health problems. And who ends up practising therapy?

Do we need more people of colour and immigrants, more LGBT, working class and disabled counsellors? Researchers at the University of Virginia found that 25 percent of white resident doctors surveyed believed that "blacks' skin is thicker than whites'", and many studies show that black patients are often given less painkillers than white patients – their pain is perceived to be less painful, somehow. How accessible is counselling to a poor black woman, who can't afford the £25-£70 a week for private counselling, but who is told by her GP to grin and bear it – that her years-long bipolar disorder is probably just a bad patch that will soon pass?

**

Let's say you're open to the idea of counselling. How can you figure out whether talking therapies might help you, or what kind of therapy you might be best suited to? There is plenty of reading material out there about the different kinds (person-centred, cognitive behavioural therapy, couples counselling), who they're for, and what they entail. Centres like the Cornerstone are typically happy to help (Gail often receives emails from people asking for direction). But what if you don't have access to that? Or what if, for personal and/or structural reasons, you will never have the means to attend talking therapies? It can't replace professional, focussed, one on one help, but there are a lot of resources for self help out there, says Gail. "The difficult thing is sifting through to find the stuff that's right for you." There are the official websites of charities and local initiatives, which might provide you with articles or direct you to forums, and "libraries – they stock a lot of self help books. If you pick up a book and it doesn't make

sense to you, just put it back on the shelf. Maybe next year it will make sense to you, or maybe it isn't the right kind of book for you. Don't feel as though somehow there's something wrong with you. Just look for another one, until you find the one that speaks to you."

Some people will never be able to afford counselling. Others won't have time. Some might need a counsellor of their faith, their race, or their background, or might never think themselves worthy of help. More still might never break away from the stigma which stops them picking up the phone. The Cornerstone is only one centre, in one city, in one ordinary house. But for people like me who have stepped foot inside and sat across from one (or maybe two, or three – they encourage you to find the right fit) of its counsellors, it is a lifeline. "We've all got funny little ways, and we can learn to find ways that are healthier for us," says Gail, echoing the sentiments I hear from my own Cornerstone therapist each week, "I think that if I could give everyone in the world a gift, it would just be: you're OK."

are about one and the same

who am I without it

THE BURDEN OF FALSE STRENGTH

Black women are rarely allowed to be vulnerable. **Christine Pungong** looks at the demands that our society makes on women like her, and what it means to be mentally ill and black today.

"I am a reflection of my mother's secret poetry as well as of her hidden angers."
- Audre Lorde

I've never seen my mother cry. When I was younger I came to the conclusion that she was cold, but with time I realised this simply wasn't true. I know my mother is emotional: I've seen her joyful, I've seen her furious, I've seen her excited and scared and even sad – I've just never seen her cry. I later grew up to understand that we live in a world that doesn't grant black women vulnerability – and that black women everywhere suffer for it immeasurably. It is for this exact reason that I couldn't admit to myself that I was ill for a very long time. I associated vulnerability with weakness, and as Meri Nana-Ama Danquah writes in her memoir *Willow Weep For Me*, "weakness in black women is intolerable". In a way, that's what made borderline personality disorder, or BPD, an even more terrifying diagnosis – emotional instability is not in the black girl repertoire.

BPD is characterised by unstable emotions and relationships, impulsivity, self-harming behaviour and disturbed thought processes. BPD has always been a complex and controversial diagnosis among clinicians. Some (like my old psychiatrist) even refuse to refer to it as a mental illness, and instead acknowledge it only as "a series of maladaptive behavioural patterns". These people, regardless of who they are, are terribly misinformed.

Unlike anxiety or depression, it's not so easy to pinpoint any exact things that I do, or think, and attribute them to having BPD. It influences every aspect of my life and my reality. It

113

Historically, the value of black womanhood has rested on our ability to endure pain in silence. Black women are martyred for their ability to silently withstand the violence and injustice enacted upon them; apparently it is what makes us divine

affects all of my actions, interactions and relationships. It also means I spend a lot of time worrying about how I can ever separate myself from it. What parts of my personality are me as an individual and what parts are just the pathology? Are they one and the same? When your identity is constructed around an illness, you can't help but ask yourself: who am I without it?

For a long time, I thought that a personality disorder was a life sentence, when in fact many patients with BPD achieve either full or partial remission within 10 years. Sometimes that feels too long to keep pushing for. At other times it gives me something to strive towards. While it's been clear to me that I've had BPD since the age of 15, I only pushed for an official diagnosis a year ago, when I was positive that I had the physical and mental energy to confidently discuss and advocate for my own health. I already knew from the experiences of friends and family that manoeuvering the mental health system as a black woman was tough. You are gaslighted, patronised, ignored or just completely forgotten about. But still, I naively anticipated that the aftermath of my official diagnosis would bring a wave of relief, comfort and reassurance. I eagerly awaited the peace of mind, but it never came.

The first time I approached a doctor with the idea that I might have BPD, he told me that if I thought I had it then it was most likely that I didn't. For good measure, he felt the need to add that patients with BPD were often difficult, stubborn and untreatable, and he didn't think I was any of those things. I remember being shocked, if not disturbed by his antipathy; little did I know of the stigma that would await me post-diagnosis. Hospital A&E staff don't treat you with quite the same care or attentiveness, GPs refuse to offer you certain medication, nurses audibly sigh when they read your file. Despite being medical professionals, none of them even try to hide their distaste. The internet doesn't prove to be any more reassuring. The first time I googled BPD I was bombarded with pages and pages of unwarranted stigma and abuse. Articles on how awful and manipulative those with BPD are, and forums with tips on how to avoid us.

A lot of BPD stigma stems from the fact that its symptoms aren't as palatable or acceptable as people would like them to be. They exceed the limits of a lot of people's so-called sympathy and compassion for mental illness. While in recent years mental health awareness has boomed, all that's really happened is that stigma has shifted from what are now slightly better understood conditions like anxiety and depression, to the less pleasant ones – meaning personality disorders, psychotic and dissociative disorders, bipolar disorder and so on. Statistics show that seven in every 1000 people in the UK have BPD. Why are we still treated like we are undeserving of care?

Being a black woman adds an intense extra dimension to that. Healthcare is both racialised and gendered, and yet many mental health professionals who I have met seem to find it difficult to comprehend the role racism and sexism can have in causing and worsening certain mental illnesses.

You'll find "when is the right time to tell the person you're dating that you have a personality disorder?" in my recent Google search history

Sometimes I'm aware of my illness being almost political. The anguish and suffering of black women is fetishised only when it's in sacrifice. Historically, the value of black womanhood has rested on our ability to endure pain in silence. Black women are martyred for their ability to silently withstand the violence and injustice enacted upon them; apparently it is what makes us divine. The harm this does to the mental health of black girls everywhere is traumatic.

A study published in the *British Journal of Psychiatry* in 2010 that was conducted in the emergency rooms of three cities showed that young black women were the demographic most at risk for self-harm. There's no way to turn that into poetry. At this point in my life I empathise with my mother more than ever. I recognise now that she was probably never even given the space she needed to cry. Did anyone ever think to ask her: are you OK? What has happened to you? What are the ways in which I can help you heal? More than anything I want my mother to be free from this burden of false strength.
With this in mind, I refuse to feel selfish for devoting my undivided care and attention to myself. I refuse to feel selfish for talking unashamedly about my illness. I repeat those two sentences to myself every single day. It is an act of political warfare to put myself first.

Having a complex mental health history sometimes feels like I'm carrying around some sort of secret. You'll find "when is the right time to tell the person you're dating that you have a personality disorder?" in my recent Google search history. I once dated someone who insisted, without prior knowledge of what BPD actually was, that it had probably helped me become a better person and that without it I "probably wouldn't have as many accomplishments". They saw my BPD as abstract, as something exotic and alluring, rather than debilitating and exhausting. Needless to say, we didn't last very long. The fetishisation of mentally ill people is nothing new. Society loves that particular vulnerability that comes with madness.

What that means, though, is that mentally ill people, particularly mentally ill women and non-binary/gender non-conforming people, have a disproportionately higher risk of being subjected to violence and abuse. Most of the time, the admission of my mental illness doesn't even come from my mouth – my skin reveals all my secrets. It's hard to come to terms with the fact that my scars tell my story before I get to. They imply tragedy. They suggest violence, trauma, pain. Even harder than accepting this is realising that most of the time I don't even feel safe in the one place I should be able to take refuge – my own body. I rightly refuse to allow others to weaponise my body against me, but I don't know how to stop doing it to myself.

Though I try to resist it, I sometimes get the urge to self-sabotage purely out of rebellion. In a diary entry from over a year ago I had written: "I wish I could be sicker in scarier and more dangerous ways, so then at least people would take me seriously." Of course this isn't true, but at the time it made perfect sense. In a world that doesn't give me the space to be in pain, let alone listen to why or affirm it, surely the greatest thing I could do is deteriorate, and make a spectacle of it too – do it loudly and violently and in protest. I know now that the exact opposite is true.

The greatest thing I can do for myself in a world that invalidates my experiences, identity and existence is to love myself fiercely, and care for myself as best as I can. I know this, but it feels devastatingly difficult to put into practice. How do I love myself when I'm not sure that I even like myself? Prioritising my self-preservation over self-destruction is my first simple step. Each new day I am learning to take it from there.

Time to Change recently reported that **80% of black and minority ethnic (BME) people feel unable to speak about their experiences of mental ill health**. When BME people did seek help, **nearly half reported discrimination** from the mental health staff they had contact with. According to *The Guardian*, black men in the UK are **17 times more likely to be diagnosed with a psychotic illness** than their white counterparts. Research focusing on black women is rare. In Lambeth, 26% of the population is black (one of the highest concentrations in the country) but **black people make up 70%** of the residents in secure psychiatric units. The Centre for Mental Health puts this huge disparity down to: **institutional racism**, stereotyping by frontline professionals, generally higher levels of economic hardship, fear and suspicion among African-Caribbean communities about mental health services and the lack of availability of culturally competent services.

THE MANY FACES OF EATING DISORDERS

Do you think you know what eating disorders look like? There's a common misconception that those with eating disorders are all the same, namely: thin, white, teenage girls. The real faces of eating disorders are diverse. Anorexia, bulimia, binge eating disorder and body dysmorphia can affect people of any gender, race, size or age. We chatted to some of these forgotten faces.

Art by **Julia Scheele**

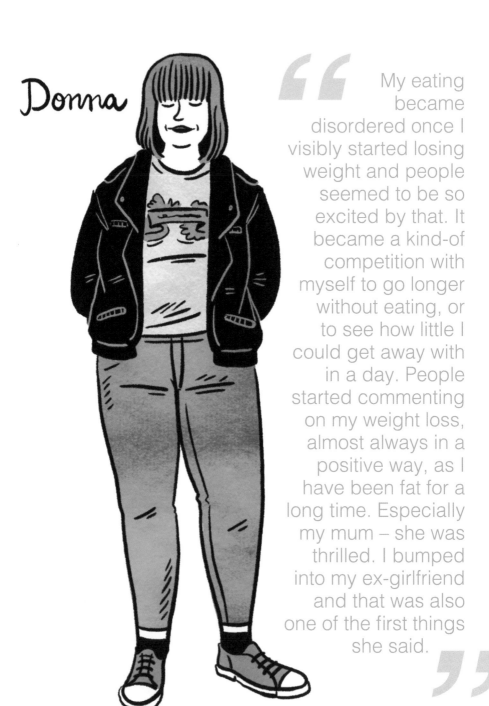

Donna

"

My eating became disordered once I visibly started losing weight and people seemed to be so excited by that. It became a kind-of competition with myself to go longer without eating, or to see how little I could get away with in a day. People started commenting on my weight loss, almost always in a positive way, as I have been fat for a long time. Especially my mum – she was thrilled. I bumped into my ex-girlfriend and that was also one of the first things she said.

"

I became incredibly strict about what I would eat and when, and would want to have control over making my own food. I think services for eating disorders are generally geared to help women in a way that can sometimes exclude men. I remember doctors saying: "Why would you want to look slim? That's not what men want." I struggled to get a diagnosis.

I couldn't eat any fun foods anymore and food was a constant obsession and stressor. I was never diagnosed with an eating disorder because I was still a 'normal' weight, but it no longer felt like the light dieting I had done before.

James

Glenys

Maria

My binge eating disorder tends to manifest as an incessant stream of thoughts and cravings, about food and bingeing, that I feel I have to battle against every minute of the day. Sometimes – often – I give in. I can't stop thinking about food, and still see it as a way to cope with everyday life. Sometimes eating is the only way I feel truly able to be free. We're all aware of anorexia and bulimia, but when your eating disorder takes your weight to the heavier end of the scale, you're just seen as greedy or having a lack of willpower, rather than it being a genuine problem.

Sophie

I used to have this fixation with being under a certain weight, with a specific waist measurement, and I would skip meals to try to achieve this. I just started my first year of uni and I trialled for uni hockey, and got in. The training and my team give me a reason beyond myself to look after myself (massive cliché I know, but if it helps) and hopefully by making steps forward in my physical health, I can work on my mental health too.

"I think many in the gay community, myself included, try to base our body on the type we are most attracted to in others. I've always wanted a slender torso, with defined abs and a hairy chest. When I became sexually active, I was drawn to men with six packs, despite how envious and self-conscious I felt around them. Body dysmorphia is not a rational illness. Many people have said things like "But you're so beautiful!" or "I never imagined someone like you could feel this way". I appreciated the compliments, but also felt slightly irritated by them. I don't think people realise that it could affect anyone."

Sean

Lowie

"I'm agender and bisexual, and struggle with feeling as though my body should look as gender neutral as I feel. People compliment my 'boyish' figure and thin legs because it's idealised. It makes sense to them when they learn I'm agender, but it just continues this cycle. I feel like I have to present myself as an androgyne because if I look 'neutral' in gender, then it legitimises my gender identity, which is still not considered real by so many people."

In my first year of university I gained weight. I came back home to Kuala Lumpur and was pressured by my mum to go on a diet pill and weight loss shake regime. Being a heavier Chinese girl is not an easy thing. Growing up in South East Asia (first Kuala Lumpur, then Bangkok) was a struggle. My body was perceived by others (and myself) as unconventional – I read a phrase in a book once that summed it up: "unfashionably curvy". Watching my schoolmates do things like model and compete in *Miss World* and *Miss Thailand* didn't help much. It hurts that such a thing matters to me.

Brenda

I spoke to a counsellor about my eating habits and thoughts around eating. While this was ultimately a positive and helpful experience, one of my strongest memories is of my (male) counsellor telling me "men like curvy girls". In addition to being totally inappropriate, at the time I identified as a lesbian. Even so, my body issues were not about how other people perceived me. It was about how I perceived myself.

Belinda

Natasha

" In my case, body image isn't really a big issue. It's more like a block in my head that stops me being hungry. I'll spend ages preparing something I love to eat and making it look nice and feeling hungry for it, but once it's in front of me and I've taken a few bites, eating can become forced. Once I give up, I'm hungry again. It's as if food is intimidating, no matter how much I love to cook and eat. I think it's difficult for some family members, being warm, homely, African women, to imagine that I feel like I can't eat, so to them it comes across as laziness, or as me being 'fussy'. "

When I came out as a transgender man, I was fat. A lot of people (including medical professionals) told me that being fat was a sign that I was unhappy and maybe I wasn't really trans. It was incredibly hard to get anyone to take my gender seriously – it felt like they couldn't see through to me, they just saw a fat person. I buy into the social construct of gender as hard as I can. To look more like a 'man', I have to have broad shoulders and no curves. I'd like to eat what I want, like pizza and pasta and KFC, and have people respect my gender and believe that I am a man. I feel like I can only have one or the other.

Blue

Bev

I've been on a diet for as long as I can remember. Once you've had kids and grandkids, being on a diet feels like the most normal thing in the world. All of my friends are on Weight Watchers. I know calories inside out, and I can't stop thinking about the foods that I've forbidden myself from. I love cooking, and sometimes I cook a feast for my family, but I make myself something different. I'd love to be able to just eat what and when I want, but it's not that easy.

Many thanks to Donna, Maria, Lowie, Brenda, Belinda, Natasha, Blue and Bev.

James Downs campaigns for better awareness of eating disorders. Find him on Twitter *@jamesldowns*. **Glenys Oyston** is a registered dietician and Health At Every Size advocate. She blogs about a world without dieting at *daretonotdiet.com*. **Sophie Butcher** is a blogger and has written about her experience of binge eating disorder at *sophiefbutcher. com*. **Sean Mackenney** is a non-fiction writer living in New York. You can find his article *I'm A Man In The Grip Of Body Dysmorphia* on the Huffington Post website.

MY DAD'S DAD'S DAD
MY DAD'S DAD
MY DAD
& ME

The men in **George Almond**'s family don't talk
about their emotions, and George has been
left bearing the weight of the things left unsaid.
He explores how toxic masculinity has been
passed down through the generations, and
wonders how he can stop it.

One of my earliest childhood memories is of meeting my Great Grandad John
at his retirement home. I was terrified, as I'd heard he had a wooden leg and
my grandad had told me that he flicked elastic bands from it "at naughty
young boys!". This was, of course, Grandad's sense of humour, which
went a little over my head aged five.

Grandad Paul, as I called him, was my father's father. When
his father, my great grandad John, died in 2007, he
took it upon himself to write the obituary. I came
across it again over the Christmas break. It's
a special piece of writing, and not

only because my great grandad led a fascinating and turbulent life. It's
special because my grandad writes with tenderness and eloquence, yet
he writes about a difficult man with whom he had a difficult relationship, and
he pulls no punches. I've summarised it here, with quotes from the obituary:

John was *brought up in penury by a fierce mother and a loving but spendthrift
and alcoholic father*. He spent time in orphanages after his own father died

young, but he taught himself to read and worked hard. *His life changed dramatically for the better when he met and married his beloved wife Susan in 1935… She was the greatest influence on his life as she tried to civilise this small, articulate – some would say foolhardy – young man.* In World War Two, he left his young family in Lancashire to volunteer with the RAF. When he was 33, his plane was shot down over Norfolk and he lost one of his legs. John struggled to adjust back to civilian life, but he eventually settled back into society, and before too long he had grandchildren whom he and Susan doted on. *All remember with affection polo mints, seeing the ducks and being made to enjoy John's tomatoes and home-grown strawberries!* However, John was *a proud man, who could not easily control his emotions, nor accept help.* Later in life, John disowned one of his sons *in a foolish, prideful way... he was diminished not only in his innocent grandchildren's eyes, but also in the rest of the family.* He died peacefully in his sleep shortly after his 95th birthday. Grandad Paul died aged 70, just one year later.

***

I didn't grow up in penury, far from it. But I have experienced anxiety and depression, most strongly during my final year of university. I spent seven sessions with a counsellor, and much of these sessions was spent discussing my relationship with my dad. Like his own grandfather, my dad is bad at dealing with his emotions and has anger management issues. He isn't entirely unaware of this – in fact, one of my dad's many good characteristics is charity: he is quietly generous, as if to try and make amends for his outbursts. But growing up, compliments from dad were scarce and my mum, brother and I often bore the brunt of a stressful day at work. There was the constant fear that he might explode at teatime. The trigger could be me holding my knife wrong, or mum allowing my brother to pass on his peas, but even from a young age I knew that the outbursts were never really about gastronomical etiquette. Thankfully, he was never physically violent, though I still feared him right up until the day that I left home for university.

In rare moments of candour, my dad will admit that he was "sometimes harsh". He usually follows this up with, "you have no idea what it was like growing up under Grandad Paul," while giving no details away.

This never seemed fair to me. Nonetheless, I was always curious about what he was alluding to and a couple of years ago I found out. It was summer, and I was having a cup of tea with my aunt in her garden, when I opened up to her about my relationship with my dad (her brother). She, in turn, spilled the beans about Grandad Paul. He could be mean. He would use a belt sometimes. He once dragged my aunt downstairs by the hair, and on another occasion he left her on the side of the road and drove off as punishment. I don't doubt that my dad experienced similar terrors, though I'm sure we'll never hear about them from him.

My brother was unsure about me writing this piece. He never met John and was only twelve when Grandad Paul passed away. Like me, he only has fond memories of Grandad Paul. Grandparents often get to play the good cops to the parents' bad cops, don't they? We remember our grandad as warm, comforting and funny. My brother doesn't want his few memories of Grandad Paul to be overshadowed by my aunt's revelations. He doesn't want to only think of him through the lens of toxic masculinity, and neither do I.

But I wanted to write this because I believe we owe it to ourselves to open up about familial difficulties, whether with a counsellor, with our friends, or in writing. We owe it to ourselves to share what we've learned. And what do I believe I have learned? Well, if I am the first in countless generations of men to overcome the trappings of toxic masculinity, it is by little design of my own. Though far from perfect now, the world was a different place one generation ago, let alone three. Great Grandad John probably had post-traumatic stress disorder from his time with the RAF, and the horrors he experienced there. Imagine if he'd had access to a counsellor who could have identified and helped him with it.

Like my grandad, I understand that circumstance plays a part in making our fathers the way that they are. For me, the way my grandad wrote Great Grandad John's obituary shows that he was aware of social determinism – that a difficult parent, or a difficult life, can forge a difficult person. He uses the history to help explain, but not to excuse, the nastiness. My dad, on the other hand, seems to fully forgive his father any nastiness because he believes it was normal for the time. He would often caveat any harshness against my brother and I by alluding to the fact that his father was harsher on him, conveniently ignoring contemporary parenting norms.

Learning what I have about Grandad Paul, I find myself feeling sorry for my dad. But, as with Grandad Paul and Great Grandad John, I find it hard to fully forgive him. Toxic masculinity explains, but does not excuse my dad's faults as a parent. He could have looked to his contemporaries more. He could have at least persevered past the first and only anger management session he went to, instead of declaring it "a load of hippie bollocks".

When suicide is the biggest killer of men under 50 in the UK, toxic masculinity is a health crisis. It is a silence that keeps men apart from each other and even from their own emotions. It allows, even encourages, the same mistakes to be made again, and again, and again, through generations of invulnerable men. But although they elude so many, for many reasons, I feel lucky that I was born into a time where there are more places than ever for men to open up emotionally. Unlike my dad, I've formed meaningful, open emotional bonds with many people outside the insular world of family. I am close enough with my friends to be able to ask them personal questions about their relationships with their parents, giving me a sense of perspective which my dad probably never had. Without this, and without my counselling sessions, I don't think I would ever have truly questioned my dad's outbursts. And I am all the better for having questioned them, and for having considered the effect that my relationship with my dad has had on me. I've learned a lot exploring my family history. When it comes time to write my dad's obituary, I might take after my grandad. When it comes to being a father, I won't.

MEN ACCOUNT FOR OVER THREE QUARTERS OF DEATHS BY SUICIDE IN THE UK

THEY MAKE UP ONLY 36% OF THOSE ACCESSING PSYCHOLOGICAL THERAPIES

95% OF THE PRISON POPULATION IS MEN, AND 87% OF ROUGH SLEEPERS

MEN ARE NEARLY THREE TIMES MORE LIKELY THAN WOMEN TO BECOME ALCOHOL DEPENDENT, AND THREE TIMES AS LIKELY TO REPORT FREQUENT DRUG USE

MEN HAVE MEASURABLY LOWER ACCESS TO THE SOCIAL SUPPORT OF FRIENDS, RELATIVES AND COMMUNITY

FACTS AND FIGURES FROM: ONS, NHS, HOUSE OF COMMONS LIBRARY, CRISIS, HEALTH AND SOCIAL CARE INFORMATION CENTRE AND GOV.UK

The word 'crazy' has a long history of being used to silence
and invalidate the experiences of mentally ill people.
Anna Leszkiewicz looks at how it's women who often bear
the brunt of this, and at the TV shows turning that stigma on
its head. Art by **Verity Slade**.

When I have a particularly bad day, one that leaves me feeling more like a
sad little raisin than a human person, I slump home and put on the same
record: *Crazy* by Patsy Cline. You know the one. Two minutes and 45
seconds of pure heartache, Cline recorded her vocals in a single take; the
result is a howl of vulnerability that has struck a chord with millions (it's often
considered one of the greatest songs of all time).

In it, Cline announces, "I'm crazy," and proceeds to list all the reasons why.
She's crazy for feeling lonely, for feeling sad, for worrying, for trying to make
a relationship work, for believing it would work, for crying over it – and, most
of all, for being in love. She's crazy, in short, for being a woman who feels
the full spectrum of human emotion.

Crazy stormed the charts two years before Betty Friedman's *The Feminine
Mystique* identified "the problem that has no name" – the widespread misery
of women in the 1950s and early 1960s. It speaks to a time when any normal
negative emotions in women were pathologised. The perfect 50s housewife
was blissfully, blithely happy, or she was crazy – there was little room for
anything in-between.

The obsessive, unpredictable, emotional woman has been a trope on
screen for decades. From *Sunset Boulevard* to *Fatal Attraction* to *Single
White Female*, 'passionate' female characters are often only a few steps
away from extreme violence. And as long as women who feel anything at
all have been characterised as hysterical, women have been resisting the
label 'crazy'.

133

The theme for Rachel Bloom's CW series *Crazy Ex-Girlfriend* is a case in point. It features a chorus of animated versions of the lead character's friends singing, repeatedly, "She's the crazy ex-girlfriend", while Rebecca (played by Bloom) interrupts with objections. "That's a sexist term," she insists. "The situation is a lot more nuanced than that." Over and over throughout the first season, Rebecca protests that she's simply not 'crazy'.

'Crazy' is, of course, a derogatory, dismissive term used to stigmatise and silence. But mental health problems are real, and our society does have a gendered problem in the way it understands mental health. So where's the middle ground? How do we reject decades of oppressive stereotypes whilst also making space for sensitive portrayals of women with mental health problems on screen?

It might not seem the instinctive place to find the best material on the subject, but TV comedy is providing the perfect home for more long-term, evolving explorations of women's mental health: several current shows start with the typical image of a 'crazy' woman, and then, over time, deconstruct the trope in front of us, and even begin to reclaim the word itself.

Crazy Ex-Girlfriend begins with a single, crazy plot point – woman moves across country to be near an ex-boyfriend she hasn't seen in a decade – and

gradually unpicks it, until we begin to understand that Rachel's move really has a lot more to do with her complicated emotional state, past traumas, and years of mounting stress than it does with her crush on Josh.

E4's *Crazyhead* follows two young women, Amy (Carla Theobald) and Raquel (Susan Wokoma), who have the ability to see humans who are possessed. They're also both receiving psychiatric care, are on and off various medications, and are convinced that a trained psychiatrist is the figure behind this supernatural conspiracy to bring them down. The show neither insists that supernatural forces are the only explanation for Amy and Raquel's perceived 'craziness', nor does it paint them as unhinged stereotypes. In this horror show, they fight demons both metaphorical and literal at the same time: Amy and Raquel can experience anxiety, paranoia, and even hallucinations, and simultaneously fight supernatural forces no one else can see.

Or take Suzanne (Uzo Aduba) from *Orange is the New Black*. First only known as Crazy Eyes, Suzanne begins her life in the show as a caricature: obsessively overfamiliar, violent, incapable of empathy – with the viewer given no specific diagnosis, just a general suggestion of 'craziness'. But as the show develops, we see so much more to Suzanne – her emotional intelligence, her creativity, her vulnerability, her capacity for love – without skirting around the fact that she still struggles with her mental health. All of

these shows take the meaningless, offensive label of 'crazy' and slowly, but surely, take it apart.

There are more specific explorations of women's mental health, too. Phoebe Waller-Bridge's *Fleabag* begins as a seemingly straightforward comedy about a brash, sexual young woman – but as the series develops, it increasingly becomes an intimate portrait of grief and the way it can intersect with existing mental health problems to devastating effect. *My Mad Fat Diary* offers a look at disordered eating that is a million miles away from the dreamy, nymph-like anorexic we've seen in shows like *Skins.*

Over several seasons, *You're The Worst* has explored how relationships can both falter and flourish when both partners suffer from depression. *Unbreakable Kimmy Schmidt* examines the effects of post-traumatic stress disorder, years after the original trauma itself, while the final episodes of HBO's *Insecure* began to explore how issues of gender, race and mental health intersect. Oh, and all these shows are really, really funny – thoroughly rejecting the idea that investigating mental health is always doom and gloom.

We still have a long way to go in portraits of female mental health on screen: these characters are rarely given concrete diagnoses, their symptoms often sensationalised, and we're still only really seeing the 'acceptable' face of mental illness: the true breadth of neuroatypical people is far from being accurately reflected on television.

But one of the anxieties that comes with any mental health issue is the fear of being labelled, the fear of becoming the stereotype we've all seen a million times. Sometimes, that anxiety can be so strong it can prevent you from seeking help. Accepting a problem can often be the first step – and it's a hell of a lot easier to accept yourself if you see people like you, sensitively drawn, on screen. Representation can help insults like 'crazy' lose their meaning, and their sting.

In the final episode of *Crazy Ex-Girlfriend*, Rebecca finds herself living a great cliché, the oldest crazy woman origin story in the book: she is left jilted at the altar. As she literally stands on a cliff edge in her wedding dress, onlookers crowd around her, including her father – the first man to ever reject her.

"You're crazy," he tells her.
She smiles, and shrugs. "Little bit."

FOOD
FOR
THOUGHT

PART TWO

Recipes for life from **Tejal Rao, Bee Wilson, Meera Sodha, Sarah Coates** and **Meredith Graves**. Art by **Tara O'Brien**.

CHIKIN MITO BORU
TEJAL RAO

Making meatballs can be an act of optimism. There's something about squishing the ingredients together in your bare hands, turning it all into raw, lumpy little investments in your future. When I don't feel capable of anything, of anything at all, I can usually manage to put on a podcast and make some meatballs. And by the time I'm finished, and the meatballs are all lined up on a tray, I have at least a dozen things to feel good about right in front of me.

This chikin mito boru recipe from **Nancy Singleton Hachisu** changed my life, but I was sceptical at first. The meatballs seemed to come together too quickly, in just a few minutes. And they sounded quite plain, simmered in a scallion broth with cabbage, like something an orphan might slurp in the saddest part of a 19th century novel. But no, the broth was fortifying and profoundly delicious, and the meatballs that bobbed around in it were sweet and beautiful, tender as dumplings, bright with ginger and miso.

I make it now when it's cold outside and nothing is going right and I don't want to end up with a lot of dirty dishes. I count on it to leave me with a little extra for breakfast the next day. It's delicious exactly as it is, but you won't regret making some rice to ladle the hot broth over. You can easily swap out the Chinese leaf for a small bunch of tender greens, like chard.

FOR THE STOCK
1 piece konbu (Japanese dried kelp)
6 spring onions
6 tbsp brown rice miso
¼ small head of Chinese leaf

FOR THE MEATBALLS
500g minced chicken (fattier thigh meat is best)
2 tbsp brown rice miso
2 spring onions, chopped
1 tbsp grated ginger
1 tbsp potato starch

Make the stock: fill a heavy pot with 2 litres of cold water, the konbu and spring onions. Bring to a gentle simmer. In a separate bowl, whisk the miso with some of the stock, so it becomes a lump-free liquid, then add back to the stock.

Meanwhile, make the meatballs. In a large mixing bowl, use your hands to mix the chicken with the miso, spring onions, ginger and potato starch. Use wet hands to shape about 10 glossy 5cm meatballs.

To finish the dish, first fish out the konbu. Cut the Chinese leaf into 2cm strips and add it to the stock. When it starts to simmer again, add the meatballs and cook for about 6 minutes, or until cooked all the way through. Serve alone, or on rice.

FRIED EGGS AND GREENS ON TOAST
BEE WILSON

When feeling low, I make myself eggs. Often, I bake them in a ramekin with cream in a hot oven for five to ten minutes. The whites go hazy like mother-of-pearl and you dip pieces of buttered toast into the yolk as if you are being cosseted on a chaise-longue like a sickly Edwardian child. But there are evenings when – sad or tired – even this is too much effort and I don't want to be preheating the oven or fiddling around with ramekins. A good thing to make on days like this, I have found, is a no-effort supper of garlicky fried greens and eggs. I am cheered by the way the golden yolks peer out of the forest of greens in the pan. Eating it makes me feel bolstered. The American writer M.F.K. Fisher once wrote about taking herself to fine restaurants as if she were 'a guest of myself'. I feel the same way when I eat these eggs. Tasting the rich egg against the slightly crispy greens, I feel I am doing right by myself.

150g greens, trimmed and sliced – broccoli, cavolo nero, leeks, chard, whatever you have in the fridge in any combination
2 cloves garlic, peeled and finely sliced
1 tablespoon extra-virgin olive oil and a nugget of unsalted butter
Sea salt flakes
Chilli flakes
2 eggs, the best you can afford
A squeeze of lemon
A hefty slice of bread

Serves one. In a frying pan with a lid (I use a deepish cast-iron pan) heat the oil and butter and add the greens. When they start to sizzle, add a big pinch of salt and the garlic and chilli. Smell the headiness of the garlic in the oil. Put the lid on and continue to cook until the greens have softened and gone a bit sweet – about five minutes, depending on the robustness of the veg.

Crack the eggs into a cup, slide into the pan, turn the heat off and put the lid on, setting the timer for five minutes. Put the bread on to toast. Check to see if the whites are set. If not, put the lid on for another couple of minutes. When the eggs are done, add a bright squeeze of lemon and devour. I'll leave it up to you whether you put the toast on a plate and pile the eggs and greens on top or cut the toast into soldiers for dipping. Both ways are good.

Bee Wilson is the author of *This is Not a Diet Book*

DAILY DAL
MEERA SODHA

This recipe for my mum's dal is my anchor. I started to make it when away from home for the first time at university, and reluctant to admit to my family and friends how much I missed home. Each step, from counting out the peppercorns and cloves to boiling the peppery red lentils, made me realise I could secretly recreate this little piece of home. The steam, the smells and the wonderful flavour: I could feel perfectly reassured and happy again, no matter which kitchen in the world I happened to be in.

It is one of my most treasured recipes. I crave it frequently and never tire of it. It's a foolproof dish, robust and endlessly adaptable, and it always yields a result far greater than the effort required to make it.

225g red lentils
2 tbsp rapeseed oil
12 peppercorns (optional)
4 cloves (optional)
1 onion, thinly sliced
4 cloves of garlic, crushed
6cm ginger, peeled and finely grated
½ tsp chilli powder
½ tsp ground coriander
½ tsp ground turmeric
300g tinned plum tomatoes

Serves four. In a sieve, rinse the lentils until the water runs clear, then drain and put in a deep, lidded saucepan. Add 600ml of cold water, bring to the boil over a medium to high heat, then cover with the lid and simmer gently for 10-15 minutes without stirring, until thoroughly cooked. Like pasta, lentils will be tender when cooked.

Meanwhile, put the oil in another deep, lidded saucepan on a medium heat. When it is hot, add the peppercorns and cloves if you are using them. Stir-fry for about a minute, or until you can smell them, then add the onion. Cook for 8-10 minutes, until golden. Add the garlic and ginger and stir-fry for a further 4 minutes before adding the chilli powder, coriander, turmeric and a teaspoon of salt. Stir well, then add the tinned tomatoes. If they are whole, pour them out with one hand and crush them with the other hand to break them up before they hit the pan. Cover, turn the heat down and simmer for about eight minutes. The tomatoes should look darker and more paste-like now, with little tomato juice running from them. Add the lentils using a straining spoon, then pour in any remaining water they were boiling in a little at a time, until you get a good consistency. For me, this is a fairly thick dal – thick enough to be eaten from a plate with bread – but you may prefer yours more soupy. Cover the pan with the lid again and cook on a low heat for a further 10 minutes.

Originally published in Meera's *Made in India*

SALTED CARAMEL BRIOCHE SUNDAE
SARAH COATES *(THE SUGAR HIT)*

Cooking is a transformative process. Discrete ingredients miraculously become greater than the sum of their parts, like modern day alchemy. I can take a piece of toast, a scoop of ice cream, a pile of sugar, and reinvent them with heat and time. Doing so is an exercise in perspective. Take this sundae, for example: on the one hand, this is a spectacularly delicious, buttery-salty, crispy-sweet symphony of a sundae; on the other hand it's ice cream and toast. It's a perfect illustration of the fact that something can be both mundane and wonderful at the same time, depending on how you look at it. And when I make this, I'm reminded that if that's true for the food in the bowl, then it must also be true for the flawed human in the kitchen, who is on the one hand only me, but also much more than that, depending on how you look at it. And then I get to eat.

100g caster sugar
50g butter
65ml double cream
Sea salt, to taste
1 thick slice brioche
Small handful flaked almonds
1 scoop vanilla ice cream

Place the caster sugar into a medium-heavy based saucepan, ideally of light-coloured metal so you can see the colour as the caramel cooks. Add 2 tablespoons of water and place the pan onto a medium heat. Cook, tilting the pan gently to help everything melt evenly, until a clear syrup forms, and then continue on until a deep amber caramel forms. This process takes about 5-10 minutes, but don't walk away.

Remove the pan from the heat and carefully add the butter and cream. This will cause the caramel to sputter and hiss but just wait, leave it alone, and it will calm down. Place the pan back on the heat and stir with a wooden spoon until the mixture comes back to the bubble and you have a smooth, thick caramel sauce. Turn off the heat and add about 1 teaspoon of salt, taste – carefully because it's really hot – and add more if you want it. Set aside.

Place your slice of brioche into the toaster to get a nice golden tan. If you feel like it, you can toast the flaked almonds in a dry frying pan for a bit to make them extra crisp and toasty. Once the brioche is ready, place it in a bowl, top with a melting scoop of ice cream, plenty of sauce (you'll have way more than you need – this is great news, it keeps excellently in the fridge for at least a week), and scatter over the almonds. Eat.

MORE LIFE PASSIONFRUIT TART
MEREDITH GRAVES

FOR THE PASTRY
175g plain flour
100g unsalted butter, chilled
and cubed
2 tbsp caster sugar
1 tbsp milk
1 large egg yolk

FOR THE FILLING
300ml double cream
3 large eggs
3 large egg yolks
125g caster sugar
50ml lemon juice
150ml passionfruit juice, from
6-8 passionfruit

Based on a recipe by Donna Hay. Mix the flour, butter and sugar in a food processor until it has a mealy, even texture. Add the milk and egg yolk, and mix until the dough starts to form. On a floured surface, flatten into a disc and wrap in cling film. Chill in the fridge for about 30 minutes. Drake's *More Life* is 1 hour and 21 minutes of heartbreak pop, meaning it's about perfect if you start it now.

After half an hour (sometime around *4422*), roll out the chilled dough until it's an even thickness, and big enough to cover a lightly oiled 20-22cm flan/tart tin.

Drape the pastry over your tin and press into the base and sides. Trim the edges evenly, because that's the last thing in your life over which you can exert any semblance of control. Prick the bottom of the crust with a fork. Making a nice design is a meditative practice that can stop you from crying into your pre-baked tart. Refrigerate for another 30 minutes.

Take the pastry trimmings and make little shapes – I used a fork to make leaves and some stray biscuit cutters to make little flowers. The album will be over about now. Start it again. Play *Passionfruit* on repeat for a while. It's your big special day, and you can do whatever you want.

Line the pastry crust with baking paper and add uncooked rice on top to weigh the paper down (unless you're fancy and have baking weights). Bake at 160°C/fan 140°C/gas mark 3 for 20 minutes. Remove the rice and paper, and bake for another 12 minutes, along with whatever silly meaningless shapes you made, spread out on another baking tray.

Optional: At this point, realise you're going to be really late for your first date in three years. Following the original recipe, you'd make your custard at this point and fill the still-warm crust before baking – but failing that, you can leave your partially-baked crust out on the counter for a day or two. You can also leave your pastry leaves and flowers out and wonder if your ex would see them and think a small lovely thought about you.

It's time to make the custard. Adjust the oven to 140°C/120°C fan/gas mark 1. In a big bowl, mix the cream, eggs, yolks, sugar, lemon juice and passionfruit juice. Whisk it until it's a uniform runny yellow sludge. The colour is really pretty. (The original recipe I worked from calls for you to strain the mixture, but I don't even have a colander, let alone a fine mesh strainer, so I just swirled it around looking for stray bits of eggshell, albumen, chicken toenails, whatever. Strain if you want to. You know, *yolo*.)

Set the tin over a baking tray to catch any drips. Pour the custard mixture into your crust, but Jesus Christ, be careful not to overfill it. I thought I nailed this, only to find, upon pushing the tray into the oven, that my house didn't magically become not-on-a-slant overnight. Citrusy egg goop went everywhere, dripping into the pilot light and all over the bottom of the oven, filling my kitchen with the smell of eggs and gross burning sugar. The smoke alarm went off twice. I had to open the back door and sop up Satan's steaming french toast slurry with paper towels and an oven mitt. It was disgusting, and what's more, that was last Thursday and I still haven't scraped the burnt egg streaks off the oven door. Don't pick up the pieces, just leave them for now...

Bake for 40-50 minutes, or until just set. It will still be jiggly but won't slosh if you try to pick it up. Leave to cool completely before refrigerating to set even further. If you're me, you'll refrigerate it overnight and forget it even exists because making it was a three-day process that included a lot of staring at walls and questioning how you could have fought so ceaselessly for something that was perhaps never meant to be. You're exhausted.

Listen: you never needed to make a tart this fancy. We all know it's a panacea, an expensive out-of-season charm, a choreography by which to repel ghosts. *I can't blame you now, no.* You deserve to feel useful. Maybe this is a great opportunity to learn fun new skills like tart-making. Maybe your ex did you a favour, maybe you'll become the best tart-maker in this city, maybe this tart is really just a shortcut to meeting the scruffy, butch motorcycle mechanic of your dreams who has a gnarly sweet tooth, and who can toss heavy sacks of flour over her shoulder like it really ain't shit. Your talents will someday be rewarded. She'll ask for seconds. and you will never, ever have to tell her where you got the recipe, or about what it felt like to be left. There will be sunlight streaming into your kitchen and flour on your nose, his name less powerful than cigarette smoke in the wind. You won't even burn the eggs this time. Everything will be fine.

PLASTIC MINDS

Imagining the worst is common when you live with mental health problems. It can even extend to the way you feel about the mental illness itself – the sense that your current mood will never shift, and that you are somehow 'doomed'. **Eleanor Morgan** looks at how to get out of a forever state of mind. Art by **Esthera Preda**.

Living with undulations in your mental health can be exhausting. It's so easy, during a period of distress – whatever your 'flavour' may be – to start believing your brain has tripped its own fuse.

When we've been weathering physical and psychological symptoms of, say, anxiety or depression, we get tired and desperate. Our resilience is low, even to our own thoughts. Especially to our own thoughts. The longer we suspend ourselves in the cycle of thinking that goes something like, "Nothing is working, I'm not getting any better, I can't imagine waking up with a clear mind or appreciating a good sky," the more entrenched the thoughts become. We want to blow them out like a sneeze, but can't.

This state, when we start telling ourselves we'll never feel normal again, is called catastrophic thinking, and is a symptom of many types of mental health problem. The mind clinging to worst-case scenarios. But "I'm so depressed" or "I'm so anxious" does not mean you will be depressed or anxious forever. Having an episode, or several episodes, of mental distress does not make a person de facto mentally ill.

"I feel" does not have to mean "I am."

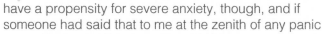

I have a propensity for severe anxiety, though, and if someone had said that to me at the zenith of any panic attack over the years, it would have gone in one ear and out the other. I'd have thought, "You have no idea." For a long time, being prone to feeling this way led to the belief that I was permanently faulty. Sometimes that thought creeps back in. However, after finally seeking proper help a few years ago, for the anxiety that I somehow managed to keep hidden from nearly everyone I knew for over a decade, I can say that my thinking has shifted.

I have written a book examining the anatomy of anxiety, which people across the world have seemed to like, and I am now retraining as a psychologist. Just as I believe that there is no finer smell on earth than the back of my dog's head, I really, truly believe that no mental state is fixed and that keeping sight of this is one of the most important things we can do for ourselves. Here are some things I've learned along the way.

Everybody 'has' mental health

'Mental health' is an easily maligned term but should be acknowledged very simply: every single one of us 'has' mental health by virtue of having a brain. A mind. We 'have' our physical health, which exists on a spectrum and is prone to faltering through infinite variables, so we try to keep things good and steady as much as we can. Mental health is a spectrum, too. Anyone, anywhere, regardless of race, religion, gender or any other difference, can experience mental distress. No one is immune and no one is 100% mentally 'well' all the time. Our mental health can be thought of in terms of how we feel about ourselves and the people around us, and our ability to make and keep friends and relationships, our ability to learn from others and develop psychologically and emotionally. Being mentally healthy is also about resilience: having the strength to overcome challenges that we all face.

A mood can just be a mood

We read about the explosion in psychiatric diagnoses like depression over the last 30 years, or how mental illness is on the rise, and obviously this is alarming. Causal links between worsening socioeconomic conditions (shout out to the Tories!) and mental distress are unequivocal, but we must also be aware of the bigger picture of what actually qualifies as pathology – something that's not 'normal' – and how subjective the notion of 'normal' is. The *Diagnostic and Statistical Manual of Mental Disorders* (DSM) is used across the world (although less rigidly in the UK compared with, say, the USA) to define and classify mental disorders. However, it is shrouded with controversy.

When Jon Ronson was researching his book *The Psychopath Test*, he met Robert Spitzer, the editor under whose charge the DSM's waist expanded most dramatically, and asked him if he thought he might have created a world in which the line between 'normal' human behaviour and psychiatric diagnoses has become dangerously blurred. "I don't know," was Spitzer's response, one as hilarious as it is scary. Because it really is hard to be comfortable with a manual hundreds of pages long that includes nebulous-sounding conditions like "sluggish cognitive tempo disorder". Are we helping people by expanding diagnostic criteria? Are we discovering problems that have always been there but were previously unaddressed? Or, are we creating new problems that now need to be 'treated'?

The diagnostic threshold for generalised anxiety disorder was lowered in the most recent version of the manual. In previous versions, generalised anxiety disorder was defined as having any three of six symptoms (such as restlessness, a sense of dread, or feeling constantly on edge) for at least three months. In the most recent version, the definition has been revised to having just one to four symptoms for at least one month. Critics suggest that this lowering of the threshold could lead to people with 'everyday worries' being misdiagnosed and needlessly treated.

On a day-to-day level, we can be so quick to label and pathologise completely normal human responses that we forget that we're human: a species defined by our thinking and emotional abilities. Periods of sadness, anxiety, bad moods, crying, etc, are part of what makes us us. Being in a bad (ie sad, nervous, irritable) mood does not mean we are depressed. Worrying about work does not mean we have an anxiety disorder. Crying, even if apparently from nowhere, does not mean we're automatically on a slippery slope to depression. (For years, I was afraid of crying. I thought that if I started, I would never stop. Now I see it like farting: holding it in is polite, possibly, but not healthy in the long term.)

Mental health professionals usually focus on the word "functioning" when it comes to diagnosis: if the way you are feeling is interfering with your everyday functioning (work, relationships, social engagements, etc.) for an extended period of time, then there may be a problem. If your mood is low, acknowledge that it's low. But also that moods, by nature, are transient. Give them a chance to pass. It is wise to be mindful of what is normal for us, the individual – the only kind of 'normal' that matters.

Brain plasticity

Plasticity, or neuroplasticity, refers to how experiences can reorganise neural pathways in the brain. We can change stuff. Long-lasting functional changes in the brain occur when we learn new things or memorise new information. This is particularly interesting when we're thinking about mental health and how easy it is to believe that we'll be stuck feeling the way we feel forever. Let's look at mindfulness meditation training as an example. You might not be interested in practising mindfulness – do what you want! – but it's a good illustration of how brains can change.

With mindfulness, you practise directing your focus to one sense, for example the sensation of your breath moving in and out of your nostrils. As soon as your attention is fixed on a physical sensation, the insula – a small region tucked away deep within each hemisphere of the brain – is activated. The insulae are thought to be where we read our physical state and instigate feelings that will make us take action, like feeling hungry then eating, to keep an internal balance. When the insulae are activated, the amygdala (the part of the brain responsible for anxious responses) settles down and our stress hormones begin to shut off. Our heart rates go down, along with our blood pressure.

Mindfulness is not something that can be taught and done in a couple of minutes, because it's the practice and repetition of gently allowing our anxious thoughts to exist while we focus on a single sense that makes the insulae stronger. It's brain body-building – you're actually building mental muscle. You can't make your biceps pop in one gym session, can you?

In one 2014 study, which looked at the way different brain regions in an individual respond to uncomfortable stimulation, researchers tested marines scheduled for pre-deployment training and deployment to Afghanistan. This was significant because military personnel are at increased risk of cognitive, emotional and physiological problems after prolonged exposure to stressful environments and would, in theory, benefit from mindfulness training.

The marines were divided into two groups: those who received their usual training (the control group) and those who received an extra 20 hours of mindfulness-based mind fitness training. All participants completed tasks during a functional MRI scan of the brain both before and after the training. Those who received the extra training showed significant strengthening of their right anterior insula and the anterior cingulate cortex, which is located in the medial frontal lobe and is another part of the brain involved in emotional regulation. It's also vital in regulating heart rate and blood pressure. Studies like this support the theory that mindfulness can change the way our brain activates and responds to negative stimuli, which may improve our resilience.

Diagnoses: how "I am" doesn't work for everyone

When we seek help or advice for our mental health, we may find ourselves hearing or using terms like "mentally ill" or "mental health problem". We may get a diagnosis. For some, having a term that they can attach to distress that has been confusing, or that they felt they had no control over, is incredibly validating. Knowing you are not alone in how you feel, and that many feel the same way, can help with feelings of isolation. It also help you to get the right, evidence-based treatment, and may lead to you joining new, understanding communities – support groups, for example. However, not everyone likes being labelled with a diagnosis. If we think about how we all have mental health that exists on a sliding scale, influenced by myriad factors in our genetics and environment – a confluence so complex that research may never be able to isolate exact causes – there are some people who won't be comfortable being told that they have an anxiety disorder. They may not see themselves as 'disordered', but rather as prone to anxiety. It's important to remember that there are many different ways of rationalising periods of mental distress. What works for one person may not work for another.

THINKING

There is a boulder on my back
rolling along the length of my spine
when I think about how much I think.
It sticks to me like a porcupine, and
pokes me whenever I try to stand
up straight. I think about dying a lot,
I think about how scared I am to die
and I think about how stupid I am
to think this. I know I can't be the
only one to think like this, to be so
preoccupied with the way my brain
will stop working one day, but this
doesn't comfort me. Instead, the
fact I know I'm not alone terrifies the
part of me that hopes my thoughts
are irrational, because if the way my
brain makes me think so much about
how my thoughts will disappear one
day is normal, if the way my brain
works is normal then it feels more
likely I will always be this way. I am
thinking about my anxiety and I am
anxious my thoughts will always be
this way, I will stay the same forever.

Words by **Bridget Minamore**
Art by **Sofia Niazi**

SEX WORK, STIGMA AND MENTAL HEALTH

The criminalisation of sex work and the social stigma that sex workers face, both in their personal lives and in their work, can make mental health a difficult topic to broach. **Molly Smith**, a sex worker and activist, explains how – through decriminalisation of sex work and the provision of non-judgmental support networks – we can help.

Some sex workers are mentally ill. Mental illness can be a factor that leads people to start sex work, because unlike many other kinds of work, sex work often has flexible hours. Or people might develop mental health problems while doing sex work – either for unrelated reasons, or for reasons related to the work (for instance, being triggered by experiencing sexual assault at work). Sometimes sex work helps people to recover good mental health, for example, if sex work enables you to move out of insecure, cold, damp housing, or if it enables you to escape your homophobic parents, or start funding your gender transition. Several of these factors can be at play at once: sex work can be good and bad for your mental health at the same time.

The relationship between mental illness and sex work can be fraught. Sex workers are often accused of being 'crazy', 'deluded' or 'broken' as a way of discrediting us. As a result, some sex workers push back by emphasising their good mental health, as a way of suggesting that they deserve to be taken seriously. These two discourses both agree that being a sex worker with bad mental health is a discrediting thing, and so they harm sex workers who are living with bad mental health – which is a lot of us.

When sex workers disclose mental health struggles to a friend or a professional, we often get a bad reaction. People freak out at us about our sex work, and demand that we stop. These assumptions, about cause and effect, foreclose the space we might need to explore the (potentially complex!) relationship between our sex work and our mental health, on our own terms. It is also, often, an impossible demand: our need to pay rent doesn't just go away because we've started struggling with our mental health, and it's unlikely that being evicted is going to help with any kind of health stuff we have going on.

Mental health is sometimes presented as 'apolitical', but the mental health of sex workers is a deeply political topic. I've already highlighted the importance of housing and healthcare. The final thing to mention is criminalisation, which is often presented as a solution (even a so-called 'progressive' solution) to sex work. Criminalisation – whether of us or of our clients, landlords and managers – makes sex workers more vulnerable to eviction. It makes us more vulnerable to assault, and to arrest. It makes us more isolated. It reduces our access to healthcare. It leads to more deportations. Resisting criminalisation and working in solidarity with sex workers *is* mental health activism!

SEEING THE COLOURS

Aamna Mohdin arrived in the UK as a refugee when she was nine. She talks about the pain that her refugee mother carries, and the legacy of hurt – and hope – that has been passed onto her. How do we build a model of mental healthcare in which the pain of refugees isn't lost in translation? Art by **Saffa Khan**.

I jumped head-first into my new world. Had I looked back, I would have seen my mum slipping away.

This is a story about displacement. About when impossible circumstances force us to leave our homes and families. It's a story about borders: the women, men, and children who overcome them, and the ones who die trying. It's a story about adjustment, and about finding the right words to describe new pain. It's the story of my mum, F, and me, A – how we lost everything we knew, and how we managed to find each other again.

***

F was 19 and heavily pregnant when the Somali Civil War started to take its toll. Already, she was no stranger to death. She was well acquainted with the tales of friends who were suddenly missing. She cried for distant cousins whose lives were violently snuffed out; and old aunties whose dignified lives came to an undignified end. *Inna Lillahi Wa Inna Ilayhi Raaji'oon.*

"Inna Lillahi Wa Inna Ilayhi Raaji'oon."

F was rubbing warm oil onto her swollen belly, waiting for her friend who had volunteered to get chocolate for both of them. She had yet to return. She never would. F struggled to come to terms with this death, to accept she would never hear her friend laugh again. Would F live to hear the sound of her child's laugh? The question spurred her and my dad into action.

It would take F a month to reach a refugee camp, which was overrun and squalid by the time she got there. During that journey, she would be captured and tortured and lose my dad among a flurry of people fleeing death and destruction. She would never feel anything as painful as the hunger that firmly gripped her throughout this grim odyssey.

"I had seen death many times, but somehow I always escaped," she told me one night, incredulously, tears slipping through her dark eyes as she laughed. Her sister, my aunt, S, jumped in, bursting to tell her own story. S had lost half her body weight when she finally found my mum at the camp. "I was so skinny," she said with a wicked smile, "your mum and dad didn't even recognise me."

"You didn't even look human," my mum added, before they collapsed into fits of laughter. I listened patiently and anxiously. My family were the masters of black humour; they always found a way of twisting pain into a joke. My smile sat awkwardly on my face. My chest tightened.

"My family were the masters of black humour; they always found a way of twisting pain into a joke."

We arrived in the UK when I was about nine, travelling through so many countries, a dizzying mix of blue, white, and red flags. We outwitted guards and slipped through border defences. We found a new home. I don't really remember much before arriving in the UK. Much of those first few years is still cloaked in darkness.

That night, talking with my aunt and me, F frantically told me how she found my father again, and soon after gave birth to me, pushing me into a barren, uncertain world. She explained how, for those first minutes of my life, I was peaceful, almost as if silently surveying my new surroundings. The world was a bright yellow. She held me close to her.

***

I wanted to ask my mum for the right words to describe the hollow pain in her chest. I wanted to ask her, "what's the right word to describe the painful wail you let out when you think the rest of us aren't listening?"

***

There is no easy translation for depression or post-traumatic stress disorder in the Somali language. These Western diagnoses remain culturally alien to my mum and our community.

"There is no easy translation for depression or post-traumatic stress disorder in the Somali language."

When she was eventually diagnosed, my mum, like so many other refugees, refused to accept the diagnosis given to her. She refused to go to therapy and take the pills that she had been prescribed. I was furious at the time – why wouldn't she take the help that was being offered? I would later realise she was never given the help she needed. How could she begin to heal when the doctor couldn't get past her headscarf, didn't understand the words she used to describe her distress, or why she turned to the Quran for support?

Communities can express trauma in different ways. To truly see the pain that displaced people carry, health professionals need to work to form new, common ground. Only then can displaced people begin to offload their pain.

Refugees need the option of accessing mental health services in their own language. These services need to be collaborative and innovative, but most importantly, they need to be culturally sensitive. They need to be built by different community members and stakeholders who can map out common problems and forge new solutions. In short, we need to learn how to support each other.

***

My family were nomads for many generations. A strong culture of migration runs through my veins. I now see the beauty in the nomadic life ingrained in Somalia's national identity. It's helped me appreciate the sheer trauma of being pushed out of my homeland and being trapped, limited and split apart by borders.

"Resettlement is a lifeline for refugees. But anxiety and fear don't just turn off once the bombs have stopped falling."

In the Dadaab refugee camp in Kenya, a word took on a new meaning to describe this suffering. Dadaab is the world's biggest refugee camp, home to 450,000 – mainly Somali – refugees, 10,000 of whom are third-generation refugees born in the camp. There is no easy English translation for the word *buufis*. The word originally meant "to blow into or to inflate", but now describes the all-encompassing need for resettlement: the feverish dreams of wanting to start a new life in a new country. Lighting a candle of hope and holding onto that heat and letting it burn you through the mundane days that collapse into each other. It describes the agony when that hope is brutally extinguished: being trapped in a refugee camp, the perimeters marked in bright orange.

Resettlement is a lifeline for refugees. But anxiety and fear don't just turn off once the bombs have stopped falling. Refugees need to find a way to deal with the trauma they've experienced and quickly learn to function in a hostile new world. They have to learn a new language, get a job, apply for the right financial support and understand the new school system. They often have to do this in overcrowded housing, under constant threat of failing to meet rent or getting enough food on the table. A Somali woman once told social worker and researcher Evelyn Lennon that she found it less stressful and more predictable dodging bullets and bombs than dealing with what researchers have called these "displacement-related stressors".

The conditions of daily life have a profound impact on whether refugees can heal. Refugees who land in supportive communities have higher odds

157

of moving on from war trauma and loss than those surrounded by stressful experiences. But support is hard to find in Western societies, where so many are blaming refugees for the growing fall-out from globalisation.

***

I held F close as she wept on my lap. I ran my hands through her hair. I learned to absorb her pain. I felt like I was going to burst into a million dark green pieces.

***

To be a child of a grieving diaspora is to carry the shock and pain of being violently uprooted, all while suffocating on hope. It's to feel too black, too Muslim, an uncomfortable 'other'. It's to feel too British, too Western, too lost in your ways. It's to feel like a stranger, hiding so much of yourself from the ones you love. It's to sit in the sidelines, carefully balancing each foot in two, separate worlds. It's to mumble words in Arabic, English, Somali, frustrated by the way they die, half-formed, in your mouth. It's to speak in an accent that robs you of your history.

"To be a child of a grieving diaspora is to carry the shock and pain of being violently uprooted, all while suffocating on hope"

I think, feel, and dream in different languages. I see the world in different colours. I feel overwhelmed by the future and its endless choices. I am stunned by the past. My mum and I are slowly building a bridge together. I firmly grip her hand as we watch our old and new worlds merge, seeing the colours run. We will jump in when we're both ready, together.

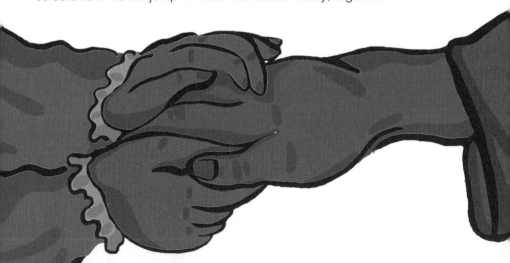

I DON'T DRINK, ACTUALLY

Anne T. Donahue realised she was an alcoholic at age 27.
Where do you go once you've hit the bottom of the bottle?
Art by **Mar Hernández**.

In May, it'll be four years since my last drink. That's a shit-tonne of weeks and about a billion more days, and I'd very much like to say I don't think about drinking anymore, but that's a lie. I think about drinking every once in a while because I liked it a lot, and that's why we're here.

I started drinking when I was 15, and at the time it wasn't really a problem. Everybody drank; everybody had a reasonable time with it. The older I got, the more I thought I was drinking 'well', not drinking 'young'. Having graduated from coolers to hard liquor to wine and gin (because I'm a lady) as years progressed, by the time I was in my early twenties, I kept myself distanced from my sloppier teen persona – telling myself that I'd graduated from the fall-over antics of my youth, with bonus points for never feeling sick or hungover. Plus, I told myself: I didn't need it.

Which was a lie. As an anxious young woman with a then-undiagnosed mood disorder, I'd begun to lean on drinking as a means of social participation. After-work drinks were a means of making and keeping friends, and particularly so as we commiserated about whatever-the-hell over too many glasses, bonding over any of the emotions that tended to pour out of us the more we poured into ourselves. I was 27 and an alcoholic.

Cliché as it might be, I didn't think I had a problem. I liked how I felt when I was drinking – even if I wished I could shut myself up or be demure or mysterious or any number of traits I couldn't be when I was drunk. I loved the familiarity of knowing that even in a shit social situation, I could have fun. I craved the comfort of knowing that if everybody was drunk together, we could still all comb through our regrets the following morning, united in hangover.

I didn't want to think about Christmas or birthdays or work dinners or lounging at somebody's house without a glass of wine in hand. I didn't want to think about meeting strangers (or interacting with

"Drinking had become a partner – a self-destructive relationship you know you should get out of, but can't because it's all you know. I was an alcoholic and now I needed to break up with alcohol."

guys I had crushes on) without the glaze of gin-induced false confidence. I didn't want to have to remove that one constant from social situations defined by unpredictable variables. I didn't want to write without the security blanket of a doubt-reducing drink or three. I wanted to drink and I still want to drink. But there came a breaking point where alcohol stopped being OK.

Living about an hour outside of Toronto, it had become second hat for me to drive home after a night out, and while I felt bad about it in a way, I didn't feel nearly bad enough to stop. But one night, I came home, went to bed, and woke up. I couldn't remember the drive. I knew I got home because that's where I was. I knew I drove there. I knew that obviously nothing terrible had happened, but that was... it. If you'd asked me anything else about it, I wouldn't have been able to tell you.

So I tried to picture my life without drinking. I tried to picture the birthdays and the Christmases and the work dinners and the dinner-dinners and the flirting with guys I liked, totally sober. I tried to imagine not having the option to down a martini or a bottle of wine, and then I started to cry. Drinking had become a partner – a self-destructive relationship you know you should get out of, but can't because it's all you know. I was an alcoholic and now I needed to break up with alcohol.

I emailed sober friends I knew, asking for advice. I was honest with friends I met up with about why I couldn't split a bottle of wine anymore. I made a stupid decision to go to a party defined by its open bar, but managed not to have a single sip. I reminded myself that during periods of sobriety in my early twenties I'd managed at parties just fine, and people waded through life without drinking all the time. It would be fine.

I began confronting my anxiety head on: my anxieties about not being a good writer sober or a fun friend sober and what it might be like to actually feel things sober. With the help of my therapist and the friends who listened, I slowly began learning that I was enough.

There are nights I'd still love a drink. When I'm anxious before a social event, or when the idea of dealing with tragedy makes me want to walk into the sea, I want nothing more than to say fuck these four years. But the thing about addiction is that you don't usually have the luxury of dipping in and out. I've never been somebody who does things in moderation: I work too much, I worry too much, I eat too much. I'm chill only when I'm in control. And when I drink, I'm not in control.

I'll just keep telling myself that I'm enough. Over the last couple of years, I'm happy to tell you that I've actually started to believe it.

it's October 18th, ten days before your 22nd birthday.

you feel heavy with luck.

these days it feels as if the architecture
of your life is being woven together by
someone who loves you very much,

who has read all your diaries,
taken careful notes on all your
dreams.

think back
ten years,

to 12

to a person you
no longer are,
but are carrying with you.

she is your passenger,
small and warm in the palm of your hand,
behind your eyelids.

you hope she likes the view.

Words and art by **Rosemary Valero-O'Connell**

CONTENTS

Discussions about mental health and illness can raise sensitive subjects which may be distressing for some people. Below you will find a list of the features in this zine with some notes on the themes they cover. You might want to use this to avoid troubling topics, or perhaps to direct you to the experiences that resonate with your own.

CONTRIBUTORS

Anne T. Donahue
@annetdonahue
Writer and person from just outside Toronto who wasted her potential for about 10 years.

Grace Helmer
gracehelmer.co.uk
Brighton-born, London-based illustrator who loves painting and staring out of the window.

Anna Leszkiewicz
@annaleszkie
The pop culture writer at the New Statesman. Her interests include dog breeds, Dorothy Wordsworth and Harry Styles's left dimple.

Molly Brooks
mollybrooks.com
Freelance illustrator and comics-maker in Brooklyn by way of Nashville. At this very moment she is probably eating jelly beans and DEFINITELY drinking tea.

Izy Hossack
topwithcinnamon.com
Cookbook author and Nutrition BSc student who likes dark chocolate, flaky salt and instagramming her food.

Sadhbh O'Sullivan
@sadhbhlikedive
Full time at Refinery29, some time writer and spare time co-editor of Ladybeard Magazine.

Saffa Khan
safka.co.uk
Pakistani queer visual artist and zine-maker, based in Manchester, creating work surrounding identity, sexuality, mental health and culture, via print and mark-making.

Sarah Chong
sarahchong.co.uk
Freelance web designer, feminist and lover of all things yellow. Fond of pandas, food and lists.

Laura Snapes
@laurasnapes
Freelance journalist and culture critic. She never knows what to write in whimsical one-line bios.

George Almond
Northern lad in London by way of Holland. More an engineer than a writer.

Ellis Jones
trustfund.bandcamp.com
Musician who plays guitar and sings in the band Trust Fund. Writing a PhD on the impact of social media on DIY music.

Bethany Rutter
@bethanyrutter
A fat writer from London who likes thinking about clothes and (fat) bodies. Loves selfies, crime podcasts and exercising in public.

Sophie Slater/Birdsong
www.birdsong.london
A brand that seeks to revolutionise the way we shop. From migrant seamstresses to unedited models, to knitting grannies, we unite women from different backgrounds.

Rosemary Valero-O'Connell
@hirosemaryhello
Currently working on a graphic novel with award-winning author Mariko Tamaki. Won her second grade spelling bee by spelling the word 'human'.

Yossy Arefi
apt2bbakingco.com
Author of *Sweeter Off the Vine: Fruit Desserts for Every Season*. Writes the award-winning blog Apt. 2B Baking Co. which celebrates seasonal baking and preserving.

Lizzy Stewart
abouttoday.co.uk
Author and illustrator, currently living in South London.

Abigale Feasey
IG: abigale91
English student from Teesside. Perfectionist, magazine addict and Yorkshire tea enthusiast. Currently waving goodbye to anorexia and chasing her journalist dreams.

Mar Hernández
www.malota.es
Illustrator based in Valencia.

Ana Galvañ
IG: anagalvan_comic
Illustrator and a comic creator based in Madrid. Her work has appeared in publications coordinated by Fantagraphics, Nobrow, Ultrarradio and more. Recently, she published the fanzines *Más Allá Del Arco Iris* (Beyond The Rainbow) and *Luz Verdadera* (True Light).

Rudy Loewe
rudyloewe.com
Queer, non-binary visual artist making comics, prints and illustrations, currently based in Stockholm.

Rose Blake
@iamroseblake
Making drawings and pictures in London.

Alanna McArdle
@alannamcardle_
Writer and musician based in London.

Ruby Taylor
IG: rubyst
London-based illustrator with experience in print and pattern designs, murals, and fashion.

Esmé Weijun Wang
@esmewang
Author of *The Border of Paradise: A Novel*, as well as the forthcoming *The Collected Schizophrenias: Essays*. Founder of esmewang.com: for ambitious people with limitations.

James Chapman
soundimals.com
An illustrator and cartoonist, mostly drawing cute pictures of animals speaking different languages in the Soundimals series of books.

Vanessa Pelz-Sharpe
@sarcastathon
Writer who lives in London with her dog Jax, and is much more cheerful than her writing would suggest. Recently released a chapbook about depression called *Waves*.

Sarah Coates
IG: thesugarhit
Writes about, photographs, designs, prepares and obsesses over food on the daily.

Jasmine Parker
jasmineillustration.com
Freelance illustrator and book cover designer at Bloomsbury Publishing. She graduated in 2014 from Kingston Uni with an MA in communication design, specialising in illustration.

Kaylani McCard
kaylanijuanita.com
Illustrator who illustrates socially aware children's books, editorial art, and afros. Her mission as an artist is to support the stories of the underrepresented and create new ways for people to imagine themselves.

Sammy Borras
sammyborras.co.uk
Self-publishes comics and music zines for the UK convention circuit.

Pearl Law
pearlillustrates.com
Illustrator, flâneuse, and zine-maker. Born and bred in Hong Kong, she now works in London, hoping to earn enough to eat her way through town.

Manjit Thapp
manjitthapp.co.uk
Manjit is a freelance illustrator based in the UK.

Charlotte Richardson Andrews
@_choobacca
Freelance journalist. She writes about music, culture and social politics from a queer, working-class perspective. Her style 50% killjoy, 50% Pollyanna.

Travis Alabanza
@travisalabanza
Black, transfemme and non-binary performance artist and writer. Currently one of the 2016/17 artists-in-residence at the Tate. Their work has appeared in a variety of venues, including the V&A, Tate, ICA and more.

Mariel NO
IG: mariel.no
Illustrator living and working in London. Her work focuses on the intersections of race, gender, and sexuality.

Julia Scheele
juliascheele.co.uk
Illustrator, comic artist, and graphic scribe surviving in London.

Leah Pritchard
@leahprit
Plays guitar for Alimony Hustle and dreams of playing *The Boys Are Back in Town* solo in a stadium one day. In the meantime, she's on her way to becoming a counsellor.

Ruby Tandoh
@rubytandoh
Essex girl in Sheffield. She knows that her soul is a cosmic imprint of Harry Styles's and that one day they will meet while wearing identical outfits.

Meera Sodha
@meerasodha
Food writer based in London. Her cookbooks are: *Made in India* and *Fresh India*.

Anna Valdez
annavaldez.com
Artist whose work includes vibrant still life paintings, reflecting the richness of the domestic sphere.

Diana Henry
@dianahenryfood
Food writer for The Sunday Telegraph. She is the author of *Crazy Water, Pickled Lemons*, *A Change of Appetite* and six other books.

Petra Eriksson
petraeriksson.com
Illustrator and designer based in Barcelona with a love for bright colours, patterns and playing around with type.

Molly Smith
@pastachips
Sex worker and activist, based in Scotland. Find her work at The Guardian.

Sofia Niazi
oomk.net
Artist and illustrator. Editor of OOMK zine and co-curator of DIY Cultures. She currently runs a community Risograph print studio, Rabbits Road Press.

Rebecca Appleton
freudforthought.wordpress.com
Researcher on a project which is working to improve mental health services for young people. In her spare time she enjoys netball, baking and running her blog.

Eleanor Morgan
@eleanormorgan
Eleanor's book *Anxiety For Beginners: A Personal Investigation* is out now.

Christine Pungong
@_christinecath
20-year-old reluctant art history student. Hesitant artist and writer. I love womanism, trap, horror movies and cooking for my friends.

Laura Callaghan
IG: lauracallaghan
Irish illustrator living in London. Her work is hand-rendered using watercolour, ink and pen, and depicts fearless women in colourful, maximalist environments. Featured in The Guardian, NYLON and Riposte.

Alex Betram-Powell
alexbpart.com
Freelance illustrator from Bristol. He works using a combination of pencils and digital media and is primarily known for record sleeves and poster art.

John Allison
@badmachinery
Comic book artist co-parenting a large child called Desmond.

Eve Archer
evearcher.com
Drawing rebellious girls who want to change the world.

Kelsey Wroten
IG: jukeboxcomix
Brooklyn-based comics artist and illustrator.

Kate Rado
katerado.tublr.com
A queer illustrator, animator, and game artist living and working in the Bay Area.

Danielle Chuatico
daniellechuatico.com
A body-positive, Filipino comic artist and illustrator.

Holly Exley
hollyexley.com
Freelance illustrator and watercolour artist painting in the Peak District.

Chloe Emiabata
chloeemiabata.co.uk
Freelance illustrator and painter, with a penchant for painting heartthrobs and atmospheric landscapes.

Heather Havrilesky
@hhavrilesky
Heather Havrilesky is an American author, writer, and humorist. She writes the advice column Ask Polly for New York magazine.

Eleanor Crewes
eleanorcrewesillustration.co.uk
London-based illustrator specialising in autographic screen-printing.

Bridget Minamore
@bridgetminamore
Writer, poet and journalist, whose first pamphlet of poetry, *Titanic*, is out now.

Clio Isadora Delacour-Min
clioisadora.com
A goofy, clammy-handed illustrator based in London. Originally from Manchester, she ended up staying in London after studying at Central Saint Martins.

Bee Wilson
@kitchenbee
Food writer and historian. Her books include *Consider the Fork: A History of How We Cook and Eat* and, most recently, *First Bite: How We Learn to Eat*.

Tara O'Brien
taraobrien.co
Dublin-based illustrator.

Tejal Rao
@tejalrao
James Beard award-winning restaurant critic, and food columnist for the New York Times.

Esthera Preda
IG: esteepreda
Illustrator currently living in Quebec city. Her art exists somewhere between ephemeral seasons, night terrors and folk tales.

Martha Rose Saunders
@mxrtharose
Psychology and sociology student and occasional writer, interested in neurodiversity, gender and mental health.

Robin Bray-Hurren
@inkysloth
Queer, trans and disabled printmaker, calligrapher and general crafter who enjoys industrial architecture and natural history.

Ha Gyung Lee
@ynjtb
Part-time foodie and full-time freelance illustrator.

Aamna Mohdin
Reporter covering migration, borders, and European politics.

Bett Norris
bettnorrisillustration.com
Illustrator and Lecturer based in Bristol. Stationery enthusiast.

Cat Sims
IG: cat_sims
Graphic artist and printmaker based in South East London.

Meredith Graves
@gravesmeredith
Musician, writer and cook living in Brooklyn.

Jessamy Hawke
jessamyhawke.co.uk
Illustrator working in ink, acrylic, watercolour, pencil and linocut-printmaking, interested in connecting drawing with poetry and literature, as well as using illustration and hand-drawn maps to document an experience of a landscape.

Rosamund Pearce
@_rospearce
A multimedia journalist for Carbon Brief. She makes graphics, interactive media and other things.

Verity Slade
verityslade.com
Illustrator based in London. Occasional painter. Disappointing bio author.

RESOURCES

GENERAL MENTAL HEALTH CHARITIES AND RESOURCES

Mind
mind.org.uk
Mind provides advice and support to empower anyone experiencing a mental health problem. They campaign to improve services, raise awareness and promote understanding. The Mind Infoline is available at 0300 123 3393, or via text at 86463.

Rethink
rethink.org
National mental health charity providing information, services and a strong voice for everyone affected by mental illness. The Rethink mental illness advice line is available on 0300 5000 927, 9:30am-4pm, Monday to Friday.

Samaritans
samaritans.org
Emergency support for those in crisis, with helplines open 24 hours a day, 365 days a year. Call on 116 123 from any phone in the UK or ROI.

Centre for Mental Health
centreformentalhealth.org.uk
Changes the lives of people with mental health problems by using research to bring about better services and fairer policies, with resources about mental illness in prison, men's mental health and the mental wellbeing of BME men in the UK.

Time To Change
time-to-change.org.uk
Charity challenging stigma and discrimination in society, with a focus on improving public attitudes and behaviour towards people with mental health problems.

SANE
sane.org.uk
Leading UK mental health charity working to improve the quality of life for anyone affected by mental illness. The SANEline is open 4:30pm-10:30pm daily on 0300 304 7000.

Counselling Directory
counselling-directory.org.uk
A comprehensive database of UK counsellors and psychotherapists, with information on their training and experience, fees and contact details.

HELP FOR EATING DISORDERS

Beat
b-eat.co.uk
Beat is the nation's leading eating disorder charity. They offer a helpline 365 days a year, operating from 4pm-10pm. Adult Helpline: 0808 801 0677. Youthline: 0808 801 0711.

Anorexia and Bulimia Care
anorexiabulimiacare.org.uk
ABC provides personal care and support for anyone affected by anorexia, bulimia, binge eating and all types of eating distress. They offer a befriending service and a national helpline, on 03000 11 12 13.

Not Plant Based
notplantbased.com
A website providing honest, non-patronising advice, reviews and stories to aid those who are prone to unhealthy eating and/or fitness habits.

Ellyn Satter Institute
ellynsatterinstitute.org
The ESI provides resources and support for those hoping to adopt, for themselves or their family, a more intuitive approach to eating.

Dare To Not Diet
daretonotdiet.com
Registered dietitian Glenys Oyston's blog about eating well without dieting.

The Fat Nutritionist
fatnutritionist.com
Michelle Allison is a fat woman and registered dietitian, writing about food and disordered eating through a Health At Every Size lens.

Men Get Eating Disorders Too
mengetedstoo.co.uk
An award-winning national charity run by and for men with eating disorders, as well as their carers and families.

WOMEN'S MENTAL HEALTH, REFUGE AND DOMESTIC VIOLENCE SERVICES

Woman's Trust
womanstrust.org.uk
Providing women-only, client-led counselling and support services to help any woman in London affected by domestic violence and abuse to overcome the mental and emotional harm, and rebuild her life.

The Women's Institute
thewi.org.uk
Providing women with educational opportunities and the chance to build new skills, to take part in a wide variety of activities and to campaign on issues that matter to them and their communities.

Bristol Women's Workshop
bristolwomensworkshop.org.uk
Introducing women to the craft of woodwork in a supportive environment. Woodworking skills can help women grow in confidence, improve their self-image, and also challenge wider society's preconceptions about what women can do.

Refuge
refuge.org.uk
The country's largest single provider of specialist domestic violence services. On any given day they support more than 4,600 women, children and men.

RapeCrisis Helpline
rapecrisis.org.uk
The helpline is open, to those who need to speak about an experience of sexual violence, on 0808 802 9999, 12pm-2.30pm and 7pm-9.30pm daily.

Sisters Uncut
sistersuncut.org
Sisters Uncut campaign against cuts to women's refuges and for better support for women in crisis.

Women's Aid
womensaid.org.uk
Providing services to support and empower women who have been affected by domestic violence to live independent lives free from fear and abuse.

National Domestic Violence Helpline
nationaldomesticviolence helpline.org.uk
The freephone 24 hour National Domestic Violence Helpline, run in partnership between Women's Aid and Refuge, is a service for women experiencing domestic violence, or for their families, friends or colleagues calling on their behalf. 0808 2000 247.

LGBT+ SERVICES

Switchboard LGBT+ helpline
switchboard.lgbt
Providing an information, support and referral service for lesbians, gay men and bisexual and trans people – and anyone considering issues around their sexuality and/or gender identity.

Action for Trans Health
actionfortranshealth.org.uk
Action for Trans* Health seeks to improve trans people's access to healthcare by raising funds, engaging with medical professionals about trans health and engaging the trans community about health issues.

UK Trans Info
uktrans.info
A national organisation focused on improving the lives of trans and non-binary people in the UK.

Stonewall
stonewall.org.uk
Works to let all lesbian, gay, bi and trans people, in the UK and abroad, know they're not alone. They provide resources on asylum rights, mental health and coming out.

Galop LGBT* Domestic Violence Helpline
For LGBT* people experiencing domestic violence. The line is open 10am-5pm weekdays, 5pm-8pm Monday and Thursday, and with a trans* specific service on Tuesday afternoons. 0300 999 5428 or 0800 999 5428.

SEX WORKER SUPPORT

English Collective of Prostitutes
prostitutescollective.net
ECP campaigns for the decriminalisation of prostitution, for sex workers' rights and safety, and for resources to enable people to get out of prostitution if they want to.

Sex Worker Open University
sexworkeropenuniversity.com
A place for sex workers to socialise, learn new skills, get support, and campaign for the rights and safety of everyone who sells sex or sexual services.

RESOURCES FOR BLACK AND MINORITY ETHNIC PEOPLE

Recovr
recovr.co.uk
A website to help black people find black therapists and counsellors who relate to their experiences. Launching soon, but open for sign-ups.

The Black, African and Asian Therapy Network
baatn.org.uk
Addressing the inequality of access to appropriate psychological services for Black, African, Asian and Caribbean people.

Sheffield African and Caribbean Mental Health Association
sacmha.org.uk
Covering Yorkshire, Humberside and Nottinghamshire, SACMHA provide specialist mental health services for BME adults.

THANK YOU

This zine could not have been printed without the generous support of our backers on Kickstarter. Our sincere thanks to the following people for putting your faith in this project before you'd even read a page:

Alistair Bohm
Cobi & Beth
Eleanor Morgan
Jayne Westwood
Rachel Fullard
Roll for the Soul (Bristol's best cafe)
Tony Cannings

With special thanks to our proofreaders, whose eagle eyes saved us from our bad grammar:

Abi Willford
Alissa McWhinnie
Odhran O'Donoghue

And our website designer, Sarah Chong.

Edited and designed by
Leah Pritchard and Ruby Tandoh